JEWISH
FOLK SONGS
IN YIDDISH AND ENGLISH

COMPILED AND EDITED,
WITH ENGLISH ADAPTATIONS BY RUTH RUBIN

WITH GUITAR ACCOMPANIMENTS BY ETHEL RAIM

OAK PUBLICATIONS

ILLUSTRATIONS

The pictures illustrating this song book were carefully chosen to represent first, the various ages, trials and tribulations, ceremonies and festivals, and artists' conceptions of the events that molded the Jewish people; and second, to show the differences of attitudes between the "old world" and the future through the contemporary.   M. A.

Music autography by Carl Rosenthal

Illustrations selected and positioned by Moses Asch

Cover drawing, the Jewish Bride, by Rembrandt

Cover design by Ronald Clyne

Production editor: Ethel Raim

2nd Printing

©1965 Oak Publications 165 West 46th St., New York, N. Y.

Library of Congress Catalogue Card Number: 65-22692

Printed in the United States of America for the Publishers by Faculty Press, Inc., Brooklyn, N. Y

CONTENTS

C. 2   CENTRAL

PUBLISHER'S FOREWORD

It was at the turn of the present century that the cultural expression of the Jews of Eastern Europe began to be affected by and have an effect upon the larger cultures of the western world. It was a process that was taking place throughout an area of the world that was rapidly changing its ancient ways. Not only the Jewish people but also other minority peoples became exposed in their art and literature to the larger western cultures -- Polish, Russian, French, English.

Yiddish became a language of communication at this time. People developed expressions, idiom and ideas in Yiddish -- and a whole literature of newspapers, plays and books grew up to contain this new expression. The language itself, originally a 17th century German dialect enriched with structures and vocabulary of the Slavic languages, was archaic, but never dormant. It dates back to the break-up of German, Flemish, and the languages of the Netherlands in the Middle Ages.

The life blood of this Jewish expression was nurtured in the hamlets and villages (called the Pale) of Eastern Europe -- and then it developed in the larger cities, such as Warsaw and Kutnow.

The Czars of Russia tried to discourage and destroy this new, budding cultural expression. As part of a program to keep the national minorities of Russia isolated and enslaved, they unleashed the bloody pogroms of the late 19th century. The world was shocked by the bloodshed and persecution -- and from this shock came an awareness that a Jewish people and their culture existed.

At the height of this persecution in the first decade of this century, President Theodore Roosevelt issued a strong protest note to Russia and reminded the world that the United States was a haven for the persecuted and neglected. With this proclamation, the influx of immigrants from Eastern Europe began and a Jewish life started to flourish in the United States.

Soon there were more Yiddish language newspapers in the United States than in Europe. A theater of note thrived, and actors such as Adler, Schildkraut and Muni were recognized as the equals of the best the world had produced. Playwrights, authors and poets created new expressions and ideas in Yiddish.

Eventually all this became part of the "melting pot" and the succeeding generations, without the experience of the persecution and the drive for self-preservation, became a part of the whole world around them.

Ruth Rubin, who put this book together, is herself of a generation at least one step removed from this background. Born in Montreal, she became aware of her heritage at an early age and she has devoted her energy and knowledge to the documentation and preservation of Jewish expression and culture. Today she ranks as one of the outstanding people in the field of social/musical anthropology. Her recording of the European Jewish village songs and expressions of the immigrant generation (Folkways FS3801) is considered one of the important documents in Ethnic Folk Archives.

Moses Asch

PREFACE

Jewish music is diverse and colorful. In their long history in many lands, Jews created several musical cultures and several languages. The Jewish musical treasure embraces songs of Oriental Jews (Yemenite, Sephardic, Persian, Moroccan, Daghestanian, Babylonian); Ladino songs and liturgical melodies of Spaniolic Jews; YIDDISH FOLKSONGS and Chasidic tunes of the East European Jews. Sacred music in the Hebrew tongue (religious folk song) is to be found among Jews the world over, and often differs musically one from the other, depending upon the community in which it is current.

Jewish secular folk song is mainly in the Yiddish vernacular. Whereas a small number of Yiddish folksongs in "archaic" Yiddish trace back to 16th century Western Europe (and even earlier), the bulk of the rich collection of Yiddish folksong relates to the past century and a half in Eastern Europe. These Yiddish folksongs reflect the many-faceted life of the largest Jewish community of modern times, up to World War II, when it was destroyed under German occupation.

During the 80s and 90s of the 19th century, large masses of East European Jews came to our shores, where a rich American-Jewish cultural life was created. Yiddish songs (folk, as well as art, popular and theatrical songs) figured prominently in this development. Although the Yiddish composed songs soon replaced the anonymous folksongs from the "old home", a rich treasure of the old Yiddish folksongs is still alive in the memory of many American Jews of East European origin. In fact, America is one of the most important preservers of Yiddish folksongs today. In Israel, following the establishment of the State in 1948, many aspects of East European Yiddish folksong have been absorbed into Israeli song and music.

This selection of Yiddish songs with singable English translations is a sampling from the many categories of Yiddish folksong. It includes lullabies, children's songs, riddle songs, poverty and work songs, dancing and drinking songs, humorous and nonsense songs, wedding songs, ballads, laments, love songs, courting and conversation songs, soldier songs, struggle songs. It includes also some ten songs of literary origin (by known authors).

Translating folksongs, however, is a serious responsibility. At best, such transmissions or adaptations can only serve as an accommodation and an aid. The translator is faced with the problems of transferring idiomatic expressions, traditional musical subtleties, specific national charm - from one culture to another. Folksongs which may have taken centuries to grow within a specific time and space, often cannot even be transferred adequately to another culture, which has had its own history and development in an entirely different time and place. Yet, translations from one language to another have always been made, and so, the attempt here was made also!

In doing so, it was my desire to pass on to our young generations, some of the songs of an "old" yesterday, which in their time and place, were once young and alive. These were the songs, which the parents and grandparents of many Americans brought with them to our land, when, in their own youth some generations ago, they hopefully came to build, with their sweat and blood, the institutions, the temples, the edifices, the diverse patterns of life, which we all enjoy today.

May this songbook help a little, to bridge the gap between the generations and may ALL enjoy singing the Yiddish folksongs of my people!

Ruth Rubin

Amol Iz Geven a Mayse

The Jews They Had a King

Lullaby. English text by Ruth Rubin, © 1964 by Appleseed Music, Inc.

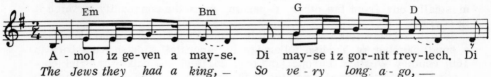

A - mol iz ge-ven a may-se. Di may-se iz gor-nit frey-lech. Di
The Jews they had a king, — So ve-ry long a-go, —

may - se hoybt zich o - net Mit a yi-dish-n mey-lech.
This is how the sto-ry be-gins my love, But it ends in woe.—

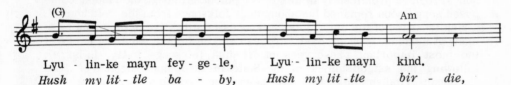

Lyu - lin-ke mayn fey-ge-le, Lyu - lin-ke mayn kind.
Hush my lit-tle ba - by, Hush my lit-tle bir - die,

Ch'ob on-ge-voy-rn a-za li - be. Vey iz mir un vind.—
I have lost my own true love, Woe is un-to me.—

Amol iz geven a mayse,
Di mayse is gornit freylech,
Di mayse hoybt zich onet,
Mit a yidishn meylech.

Refrain:

Lyulinke, mayn feygele,
Lyulinke, mayn kind.
Chob ongevoyrn aza libe,
Vey iz mir un vind!

Der meylech hot gehat a malke,
Di malke hot gehat a vayngortn,
Der vayngortn hot gehat a boym,
Lyulinke, mayn kind. (Ref.)

The Jews they had a king
So very long ago,
This is how the story begins, my love,
But it ends in woe...

Refrain:

Hush my little baby,
Hush my little birdie,
I have lost my own true love,
Woe is unto me!

The king he had a queen so fair,
The queen she had a vineyard rare,
The vineyard had a very old tree,
Hush my little baby. (Ref.)

Der boym hot gehat a tsvayg,
Der tsvayg hot gehat a nestele,
In nestele iz geven a feygele,
Lyulinke, mayn kind. (Ref.)

A branch grew on that very old tree,
In a nest on the branch, sat a little
  birdie,
The birdie chirped so hungrily,
Hush my little baby. (Ref.)

Der meylech iz opgeshtorbn,
Di malke iz gevorn fardorbn,
Der tsvayg iz opgebrochn,
Dos feygele fun nest antlofn. (Ref.)

The king died suddenly one day,
The queen, she mourned and pined away,
The branch broke off that tree, my love,
And the birdie flew away. (Ref.)

Vu nemt men aza chochem,
Er zol kenen di shtern tseyln?
Vu nemt men aza dokter,
Er zol kenen mayn harts heyln? (Ref.)

Oh, where is the man so wondrous wise,
Who can count all the stars in the deep
  blue sky?
Oh, where is the doctor, where is he?
To heal that broken heart of me? (Ref.)

Af Di Felder, Grine Felder

Over the Greenwood, on the Plain

Soldiers lament, collected by Ruth Rubin. English text
by Ruth Rubin. © 1964, by Appleseed Music, Inc.

Af di fel - der, gri - ne fel-der, Oy vey.
O - ver the green - wood on the plain, — oh, oh.

Af di fel - der, gri-ne fel-der, Dort ligt far-vor- fn a yun-ger zel-ner,
O-ver the green-wood on the plain _ Lies a sol-dier in bat-tle slain _

oy _ vey! Dort ligt far-vor - fn a yun-ger zel - ner oy _ vey!
oh _____ Lies a sol-dier in bat-tle slain __ oh. _____

Af di felder, grine felder, oy, vey,
Af di felder, grine felder,
Dort ligt farvorfn a yunger zelner, oy,
  vey
Dort ligt farvorfn a yunger zelner, oy,
  vey

Kumt a foygl on tsu fli-en, oy,vey.
Af zayn keyver optsu-ri-en, oy,vey.

Oy, du foygl, fli geshvind.
Un zog der mamen, ich bin gezint.

Fun dem toyt zolstu ir nit zogn.
Vayl zi vet nebech veynen un klogn.

Kumt der foygl tsu fli-en aheym.
Un treft zayn mamen troyerig shteyn.

Vey iz mir, oy vey un vind.
M'hot fartribn mayn eyntsig kind.

Ven di zamd vet tserinen vern.
Vet zich tsu mir mayn kind umkern.

Ven di zamd vet amol antrinen.
Ir kind vet shoyn aheym nit kimen.

Over the greenwood on the plain, oh, oh.
Over the greenwood on the plain,
Lies a soldier in battle slain, oh,
Lies a soldier in battle slain, oh.

A lonely bird comes swooping low.
Resting upon his tender brow.

Bird fly swiftly down the dell.
Tell my mother I am well.

Do not tell her that dead am I.
Bitterly she'll moan and cry.

Away the bird flew to his home.
And found his mother all alone.

Thinking only of her son.
''Where are you now, beloved one?''

When the sands will drift away.
My son from war returns that day.

Alas, the sands will drift away.
Her son will not return that day.

Ale Vasserlech Flisn Avek

All the Rivers Flow Down to the Sea

Lament collected by Ruth Rubin, English text by Ruth Rubin. © 1964 by Appleseed Music, Inc.

A - le vas-ser-lech fli - sn a - vek. — Di gri - be-lech
All   the   riv-ers flow down to   the   sea.— The ditch-es are

blay - bn ley-dig. Ni - to a - za mentsh — oyf —
emp - ty and dry. —   There's not a sin-gle soul to —

gor — der velt. — Vos zol — far - shteyn — mayn vey - tig.
lis - ten to me, —   No one to hear my sad cry. —

Ale vasserlech flisn avek,
Di gribelech blaybn leydig.
Nito aza mentsh oyf gor der velt
Vos zol farshteyn mayn veytig.

All the rivers flow down to the sea,
The ditches are empty and dry.
There's not a single soul to listen to me,
No one to hear my sad cry.

Di yorelech tsi-en, di yorelech fli-en,
Di tsayt geyt avek vi roych.
Un az ich dermon zich on dir, mayn
   zis-lebn,
Geyt mir oys der koyech.

My youth has come and now it has
   vanished,
I am left so ashamed and alone.
When I recall the days, when we both
   loved so tenderly,
I sit and I weep and I moan.

Un az a meydele shpilt a libe,
Shpiln in ir ale farbn.
Un az zi shpilt ir libe nit oys,
Kon zi cholile noch shtarbn.

When a young girl falls in love,
Her cheeks are so rosy and fair,
.But when a man breaks her heart and
   then he leaves her,
She can die of despair.

Un az di tepelech trikenen oys,
Blaybn zey ale leydig.
Un az a meydele firt ir libe nit oys,
Vert zi farfaln oyf eybig.

A jilted girl is an empty vessel,
A jug that was once filled with wine,
Oh, to have loved so well and then to
   have lost you,
To be doomed to weep and to pine.

A Geneyve

The Robbery

This nonsense song, typical of other taunts and cumulative humorous songs created by the cheder-boys, points up the abysmal poverty of their enviorment, and especially of their teacher, the rebe.

English Text by Ruth Rubin, ©1964, by Appleseed Music, Inc.

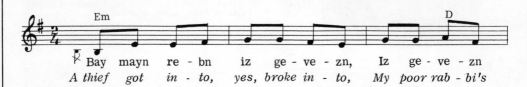

Bay mayn re - bn iz ge - ve - zn, Iz ge - ve - zn
A thief got in - to, yes, broke in - to, My poor rab - bi's

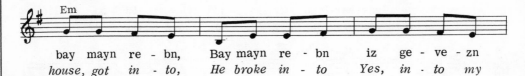

bay mayn re - bn, Bay mayn re - bn iz ge - ve - zn
house, got in - to, He broke in - to Yes, in - to my

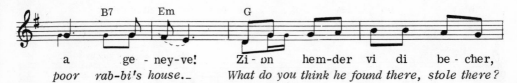

a ge - ney - ve! Zi - bn hem - der vi di be - cher,
poor rab - bi's house.__ What do you think he found there, stole there?

Dray mit la - tes, fir mit le - cher. Bay mayn re - bn
Sev - en old shirts of worn - out wool there, Three had patch - es,

iz ge - ve - zn, A ge - ney - ve!
four had holes there, Boy, what a haul! __

Refrain:

Bay mayn rebn iz gevezn,
Iz gevezn bay mayn rebn,
Bay mayn rebn iz gevezn:
A geneyve!

Zibn hemder vi di becher,
Dray mit lates, fir mit lecher,
Bay mayn rebn iz gevezn,
A geneyve! (Ref.)

Zibn laychter vi di bern,
Dray on fis un fir on rern,
Bay mayn rebn iz gevezn,
A geneyve! (Ref.)

Refrain:

A thief got into, yes, broke into,
My poor rabbi's house, got into
He broke into, yes, into my
Poor rabbi's house!

What do you think he found there, stole
   there?
-Seven old shirts of good old wool there,
Three had patches, four had holes there,
-Boy, what a haul! (Ref.)

What else do you think he found there?
 Seven candelabra, stole there,
Four - no sockets, three - no legs there,
-Boy, what a haul! (Ref.)

Zibn hener vi di tsigl,
Dray on kep un fir on fligl,
Bay mayn rebn iz gevezn,
A geneyve! (Ref.)

Zibn techter vi di sosnes,
Dray on tseyn un fir on yosles,
Bay mayn rebn iz gevezn,
A geneyve! (Ref.)

Grabbed seven roosters, red as bricks
    there,
Without heads and without beaks there,
Out the window, then he flew there -
Boy, with his haul! (Ref.)

Took the rabbi's seven daughters,
Tall and toothless, all in tatters,
Maidens all, what did it matter?
-Boy, what a haul! (Ref.)

Aylye Lyulye Lyulye

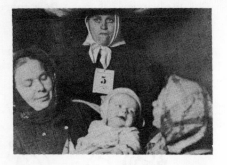

This traditional lullaby reveals the role of the working mother, who supported her males (husbands, sons) in the Jewish Pale in Eastern Europe of a century and more ago. In harmony with the mores of that time, she was making it possible for them to spend their life as scholars and pious men, thus raising the status of the family as a whole. In an environment where scholarship and piety were of primary importance, this gave the family prestige in this world and helped assure their entry into Paradise in the afterlife as well...

English text by Ruth Rubin, © 1964 by Appleseed Music, Inc.

Ay - lye lyu - lye lyu lye Shlof-zhe shlof mayn g'du - le,
Ay - li lu - li lu li Sleep my pre-cious ba - by,

Mach-zhe tsu day — ne ey - ge-lech di fay - ne.
Close your pret-ty eyes Close your love - ly eyes.

Ay lye lyu lye lyu lye
Shlof-zhe, shlof mayn g'dule,
Mach-zhe tsu dayne
Eygelech di fayne.

Un shtey oyf vider,
Mit gezunte glider,
Mayn lib-zis kind,
Gich un geshvind.

In mark vel ich loyfn,
Beygelech vel ich koyfn,
Mit puter vel ich shmirn,
Tsu der chupe zol ich dich firn...

Vest oysvaksn a groysinker,
Vestu zayn a tane!
Veln doch ale
Zayn mich mekane!

Ay li lu li, lu, li,
Sleep my precious baby,
Close your pretty eyes,
Close your lovely eyes.

When you wake up by and by,
You'll be healthy, you'll be spry,
Now you must go to sleep,
Now you must go to sleep.

I will hurry to the square,
Get some fresh rolls for you there,
I'll butter them for you,
Find a sweet bride for you too...

You'll be a scholar of renown,
The wisest man in all the town,
For your piety,
Everyone will envy me!

Bin Ich Mir a Shnayderl

I Am a Little Tailor

A sardonic conversation song, which first presents the "busy little craftsmen" of the poverty-stricken little backwoods towns of the Jewish Pale — as happy at their work. Then, it proceeds, to the rhythm of a gay wedding-dance tune, to tell us the truth of the widespread, hopeless poverty.

English text by Ruth Rubin, © 1964 by Appleseed Music, Inc.

Bin ich mir a shnay-der-l,
I am a lit-tle tai-lor, day-di-dam.
Bin ich mir a shnay-der-l,
I am a lit-tle tai-lor,

day-di-di.
day-di-di.
Leb ich mir tog - oys, tog-ayn,
I stitch and sew the live-long day, I am

Lus - tig un frey - lech un fayn.
jol-ly and as hap-py as can be.
Zog mir
Tell me lit-tle tai-lor,

shnay - der, li - bin - ker un gu - ter.
bu-sy lit-tle tai-lor, How can you sing gai - ly and mer-ri-ly?

Git dir di no - dl, ge -
Does your lit-tle nee-dle, your flash-ing lit-tle nee-dle

nug - oyf broyt mit - pu - ter? Ich mach a voch, tsvey
Earn e-nough to feed your fa-mi-ly? I work all day, go

gil - dn mit a dray - er,
wea - ri - ly to bed, —

Ich es nor broyt vayl
All that we can get to eat, is a

pu - ter iz tsu tay - er.
dry — crust of bread. —

Bin ich mir a shnayderl (2x)
Leb ich mir tog oys, tog ayn.
Lustig un freylech un fayn.
--Zog mir shnayder, libinker un guter,
Git dir di nodl genug oyf broyt mit
puter?
--Ich mach a voch, tsvey gildn mit a
drayer,
Ich es nor broyt, vayl puter iz tsu
tayer.

Bin ich mir a shusterl (2x)
Leb ich mir tog oys, tog ayn,
Lustig un freylech un fayn.
--Zog mir, shuster, hostu vos tsu
kayen?
Felt dir oyset, krigstu vu tsu layen?
--Keyner layt nisht, keyner git kayn
orves,
Ich bin a shuster, gey ich take borves.

Bin ich mir a blecherl (2x)
Leb ich mir tog oys, tog ayn,
Lustig un freylech un fayn.
--Zog mir blecher, vi groys iz bay dir
di noyt?
Hostu bulkes, hostu nit kayn broyt?
--Ich zits un klap bay yenem fremde
decher,
Bay mir in shtub rint fun ale lecher.

Bin ich mir a kremerl (2x)
Leb ich mir tog oys, tog ayn,
Lustig un freylech un fayn.
--Zog mir kremer, tsu hostu mit
vos tsu handlen?
Hostu in kreml rozhinkes mit mandlen?
--Ich hob in kreml far tsvey groshn
s'choyre,
Ich shlep dem dalis, un ich bentsch
dem boyre.

I am a little tailor, day-di-dam,
I am a little tailor, day-di-di.
I stitch and sew the livelong day,
I am jolly and as happy as can be.
--Tell me little tailor, busy little
    tailor,
  How can you sing gaily and merrily?
  Does your little needle, your flashing
    little needle
  Earn enough to feed your family?
--I work all day, go wearily to bed,
  All that we can get to eat, is a dry
    crust of bread.

I am a little cobbler, day-di-dam.
I am a little cobbler, day-di-di,
I hammer and peg the livelong day,
I am jolly and as happy as can be.
--Tell me little cobbler, eager little
    cobbler,
  What makes you sing so gaily and
    merrily?
  Does your little hammer, your awl
    and little hammer
  Shield you from the curse of poverty?
--My credit's poor, I have no funds for
    spending,
  I cobble other people's shoes, my own
    could stand some mending.

I am a little tinsmith, day-di-dam,
I am a little tinsmith, day-di-di
I fix old roofs the livelong day,
I am jolly and as happy as can be.
--Tell me little tinsmith, nimble little
    tinsmith,
  What makes you sing so gaily and
    merrily?
  Does your labor give you, a fairly
    decent living?
  Does your work give you security?
--I toil all day, fixing houses every-
    where,
  Money's very scarce, my own shack
    leaks and is so bare.

I am a little merchant, day-di-dam,
I am a little merchant, day-di-di,
I trade my wares the livelong day,
I am jolly and as happy as can be.
--Tell me little merchant, pious little
    merchant,
  Have you many things in your little
    shop?
  Do you have some almonds? Do you
    sell sweet raisins?
  Are your shelves filled to the very
    top?
--My shelves are almost empty, may
    the good Lord help us, let us pray,
  Everybody's poor in town, we only
    live from day to day...

Bay Dem Shtetl Shteyt a Shtibl

We Live at the Edge of Town

Children's song. English text by Ruth Rubin, © 1964 by Appleseed Music, Inc.

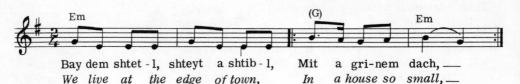

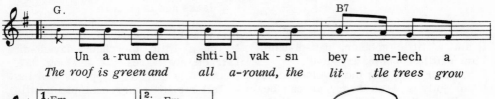

Bay dem shtet-l, shteyt a shtib-l, Mit a gri-nem dach, ___
We live at the edge of town, In a house so small, ___

Un a-rum dem shti-bl vak-sn bey-me-lech a
The roof is green and all a-round, the lit-tle trees grow

sach. ___ sach.
tall. ___ tall.

Bay dem shtetl shteyt a shtibl
Mit a grinem dach,
Un arum dem shtibl vaksn
Beymelech a sach.

Un der tate mit der mame,
Chanele mit mir,
Shoyn a lange tsayt ineynim
Voynen ale fir.

Un der tate, horevet, horevet,
Ale yorn zayne.
Un er koyft undz, un er brengt undz,
Zachn sheyne, fayne.

Brengt a hintele vos se havket,
Mitn nomen Tsutsik.
Brengt a ferdl vos se hirzhet,
Mitn nomen Mutsik.

Brengt a gendzele mit a langn haldz,
Federlech vays vi shney.
Brengt a hun vos kvoket, kvoket,
Biz zi leygt an ey!

Nemt di mame, ot di eyer,
Ay, iz dos a moyfes!
Zetst zi oyf oyf zey a kvoke:
Hobn mir naye oyfes!

We live at the edge of town
In a house so small.
The roof is green and all around, the
Little trees grow tall.

Mother, father and my sister
Chanele and me,
We've been living here a long time,
All so happily.

Father works and works and works
But I can clearly see,
He buys food and pretty toys
For Chanele and me.

He brought a puppy, barking, barking,
So we called him Tsutsik.
He brought a pony, neighing, neighing.
So we called him Mutsik.

He brought a long-necked goosey,
loosey,
Her feathers were soft and white,
And a hen that cackled, cackled
And laid an egg that night.

Mother took the newlaid eggs and
She did such a trick!
She put them under a setting-hen
And we had baby chicks!

Oyfn Yam Veyet A Vintele

Over the Sea the Breezes Are Blowing

As in Bin ich mir gegangen fishelech koyfn, this dancing song seems to conceal its sentiments under a "humorous" cloak. In fact, there are those who interpret it in a broad humorous style.

Love-dancing song. English text by Ruth Rubin, © 1964 by Appleseed Music, Inc.

Oyf - n yam vey - et a vin - te - le, Un _ di chval - yes
O-ver the sea bree-zes are blow - ing, Waves_ do bil-low and

shlo - gn. Ich hob zich far-libt in a sheyn yin-ge-le,
roll. ___ I fell in love with a hand-some young fel - low

Ch'ob nit far ve-men tsu zo - gn.
I dare not con-fide in a soul. ___

Oyfn yam veyet a vintele,
Un di chvalyes shlogn.
Ich hob zich farlibt in a sheyn yingele,
Ch'ob nit far vemen tsu zogn.

Over the sea, breezes are blowing,
Waves do billow and roll.
I fell in love with a handsome young fellow,
I dare not confide in a soul.

Ich hob zich gebovet a shtibele in vald,
Arum un arum mit fenster.
Fun ale kartinkes .vos ich hob gezen,
Biztu bay mir der shenster!

I built me a cabin in the green forest,
With windows of glass all around.
In all this world, of all the pretty pictures,
You are the loveliest I have ever found.

Tsu libstu mich fun tifn hartsn,
Tsu libstu nor mayn sheyn ponim?
Du host mich gor avekgekoylet
Azoy vi di rechte gazlonim!

Tell me you love me with all your heart,
Not alone for my pretty young face -
Oh, you have slain me, with love you have slain me,
If you leave me, I'll be ever in disgrace.

Az a gazlen koylet a mentshn,
Koylet er im mit a messer.
Host mich gekoylet un nisht derkoylet,
Bizt fun a gazlen noch gresser!

When a highwayman waylays his victim,
Money is his only desire -
But you have slain me forever and ever,
I am consumed in love's fire.

Bayt-zhe Mir Oys a Finf-un-tsvantsiger

Bandsman, Change My Twenty-Fiver Now

A well-to-do guest at a wedding, keeps tipping the bandsmen to play for him his favorite little tune. The more he dances, the tipsier he seems to get and his feet move slower and slower. His tips too, are becoming smaller...

English text by Ruth Rubin, © 1964 by Appleseed Music, Inc.

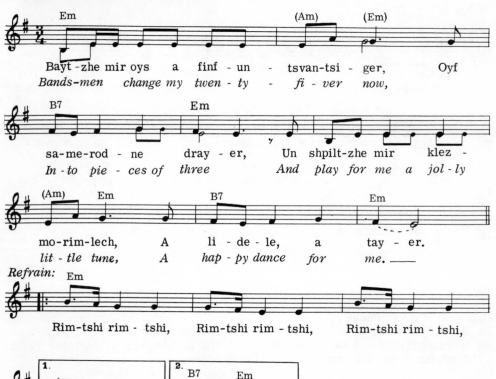

Bayt-zhe mir oys a finf-un-tsvan-tsi-ger, Oyf
Bands-men change my twen-ty-fi-ver now,

sa-me-rod-ne dray-er, Un shpilt-zhe mir klez-
In-to pie-ces of three And play for me a jol-ly

mo-rim-lech, A li-de-le, a tay-er.
lit-tle tune, A hap-py dance for me.

Refrain:

Rim-tshi rim-tshi, Rim-tshi rim-tshi, Rim-tshi rim-tshi,

1. Rim-tshi rom! 2. Rim-tshi rom!

Bayt-zhe mir oys a finf-un-
  tsvantsiger,
Oyf samerodne drayer,
Un shpilt-zhe mir klezmorimlech,
A lidele a tayer.

Refrain:

Rimtshi (7) rom
Rimtshi (7) rom.

Bandsmen, change my twenty-fiver
  now,
Into pieces of three,
And play for me a jolly little tune,
A happy dance for me.

Refrain:

Rimtshi (7) rom.
Rimtshi (7) rom.

Bayt-zhe mir oys a finf-un-tsvantsiger,
Oyf samerodne firer,
Un shpilt-zhe mir klezmorimlech,
Dos zelbige vi fri-er. (Ref.)

Bayt-zhe mir oys a finf-un-tsvantsiger,
Oyf samerodne tsener,
Un shpilt-zhe mir klezmorimlech,
Dos zelbige noch shener. (Ref.)

Bayt-zhe mir oys a finf-un-tsvantsiger,
Oyf same imperialn,
Ich vel betn di klezmorimlech,
Zey zoln zich nit ayln. (Ref.)

Bandsmen, change this twenty-fiver
    now,
Into pieces of four.
And play that lovely little melody,
As you did before. (Ref.)

Bandsmen, change another twenty-five,
Into pieces of ten,
And play that lovely little wedding dance
Many times again. (Ref.)

Bandsmen, all my money now is spent,
I haven't any more.
But if you play that sweet old tune again-
You'll have to play it slower...(Ref.)

Bin Ich Mir Gegangen Fishelech Koyfn

I Went to Market to Buy Me Some Fish

It is often difficult to categorize this type of Yiddish folksong. Is it a love song? Or a humorous song? Satirical? Dancing? Nonsense? – Actually, it contains elements of all of these types. In the environment of the Czarist Pale of Settlement, with its mores and customs of arranged marriages, love between the sexes prior to marriage, was not acceptable. Consequently, many a love sentiment, hid behind a cloak. The dancing songs, for instance, most often used love themes, which were set to the particular dance rhythm being performed.

In this song, which in the Yiddish version uses the Chasidic refrain of day-day-day, the brisk three-quarter time seems to echo the sounds of hurdy-gurdies at a fair.

English text by Ruth Rubin, © 1964 by Appleseed Music, Inc.

Bin ich mir ge - gang - en fi - she - lech koy - fn,
I went to mar - ket to buy me some fish ____

Hob ich mir ge - koyft ____ a hecht. ____ Un
They had on - ly pick - e - rels that day. ____ *May the*

ver es iz shul - dig in un - dzer li - be,
vil - lain who stole the love of my heart ____

Der zol oys - geyn vi a lecht!
Pine ____ *and with - er a - way.* ____

Day - day - day day - day - day day - day - day day - day - day
Life is so brief, my dear, Skies are so sel - dom clear,

Day - day - day day - day - day day - day - day Day.
Cher - ish the hap - py times, When love is near.

Bin ich mir gegangen fishelech koyfn,
Hob ich mir gekoyft a hecht.
Un ver es iz shuldig in undzer libe,
Der zol oysgeyen vi a lecht!

I went to market to buy me some fish
They had only pickerels that day.
May the villain who stole the love of
    my heart
Pine and wither away!

Refrain:

Day (6x) Day (6x)
Day (6x) Day, day, day, day.

Refrain:

Life is so brief, my dear
Skies are so seldom clear
Cherish the happy times
When love is near.

Day (6x) Day (6x)
Day (6x) day, day, day, day.

Az a kartyozhnik shpilt in kortn,
Farshpilt er doch nor zayn gelt.
Ich hob farshpilt mayne yunge yorn,
Finster iz doch mayn velt. (Ref.)

When a gambler gambles at cards
He risks all he's got on high stakes.
He loses money, but I lost my true love,
Lordie, how my poor heart breaks.
(Ref.)

On kayn tsigl un on kayn shteyner,
Kon men kayn hoyz nisht moyern.
Ay, s'iz nishto aza mentsh oyf der velt,
Vos er zol mich nisht badoyern! (Ref.)

Without any bricks, without any stones,
You can't build a house that way -
Oh, good people, hear my sad story,
See how I'm pining away! (Ref.)

Biztu Mit Mir Broygez?

Why Do You Pout and Frown?

Dancing song. English text by Ruth Rubin, © 1964 by
Appleseed Music, Inc.

Biz-tu mit mir broy - gez,— veys ich nit far-vos?
Why do you pout and frown, you are an-gry all day long?

Geyst a-rum a gant-sn tog— a - rop-ge-lozt di noz.
Speak to me my dear young wife — What have I done wrong?

Refrain

Day day day day day day, Day day day day.
Day day day day day day, Day day day day.

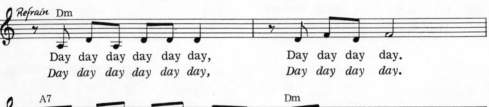

Geyst a-rum a gant-sn tog— a - rop-ge-lozt di noz.
Speak to me my dear young wife — what have I done wrong?

Biztu mit mir broygez,	Why do you pout and frown?
Veys ich nit farvos?	You are angry all day long.
Geyst arum a gantsn tog	Speak to me, my dear young wife,
Aropgelozt di noz.	What have I done wrong?
Refrain:	Refrain:
Day-day-day, etc.	Day-day-day, etc.
Un efsher vilstu visn	Would you have me tell you,
Az ich hob dich lib?	That I love you true -
Lomir beyde ariberforn	Let us go upon a journey
Tsu dem gutn yid. (Ref.)	To the ''pious Jew''.
Tsu dem gutn yidn,	He will bless us both,
A pidyen im opgebn.	A prayer he will say,
Vet er far undz got betn	We will leave a token for him,
Far a gut lebn. (Ref.)	And go upon our way.

Un az mir veln kumen
Tsurik fun gutn yid,
Veln mir beyde ariberforn
In Zelva oyf dem yarid. (Ref.)

Dort vel ich dir koyfn
A zeyger mit a keyt,
Un a sheyne groyse shtik
Zaydns oyf a kleyd. (Ref.)

To, zay-zhe mer nisht broygez
Un greyt oyf gich tsum tish –
Un zets zich mit mir esn,
Bakumstu fun mir a kush! (Ref.)

On the journey homeward,
We'll drop in at the Fair,
Where I'll buy you pretty things
And presents very rare.

We'll get a bolt of satin
For a dress and train,
Then I'll also buy for you, my dear
A golden watch and chain.

So, don't be angry, dear wife,
Come sit beside me here,
Let us eat our meal together now,
Let me kiss you, dear.

Bulbes

Spuds

Poverty song. English text by Ruth Rubin, © 1964 by
Appleseed Music, Inc.

Zun - tig bul - bes, Mon - tig bul - bes, Din - stig un Mit - voch _ bul - bes.
Spuds on Sun-day, Spuds on Mon-day, Tues-day and Wed-nes-day spuds.

Doner - shtig un Fray - tig _ bul - bes, O - ber Sha - bes in a no - vi - ne a
Thurs - day and Fri - day _ spuds. But the treat on the Sabbath is a

bul - be ki - ge - le Un Zun - tig vay - ter bul - bes.
pudding of po-ta - toes! And on Sun-day once a-gain, it is spuds!

Zuntig - bulbes,
Montig - bulbes,
Dinstig un mitvoch - bulbes,
Donershtig un fraytig - bulbes.
Ober shabes in a novine, a bulbe kigele!
Un zuntig vayter, bulbes.

Broyt mit bulbes,
Fleysh mit bulbes,
Varimes un vetshere - bulbes,
Ober un vider - bulbes.
Ober eynmol in a novine a bulbe kigele!
Un zuntig vayter bulbes!

Ober - bulbes,
Vider - bulbes,
Ober un vider - bulbes,
Vider un ober - bulbes!
Ober shabes nochn tsholnt a bulbe
    kigele!
Un zuntig vayter, bulbes.

Spuds on Sunday,
Spuds on Monday,
Tuesday and Wednesday - spuds!
Thursday and Friday - spuds!
But the treat on the Sabbath is a pudding
    of potatoes!
And on Sunday, once again, it is - spuds!

Its bread with spuds
And meat with spuds,
Breakfast and dinner - spuds!
Morning and evening - spuds!
But the special dish is always the pud-
    ding of potatoes!
And on Sunday, once again, it is spuds!

Now - its spuds
And later -spuds,
Today and tomorrow -spuds!
Week after week, it is spuds!
But the best on the Sabbath is the pud-
    ding of potatoes!
And on Sunday, once again, we get spuds!

Chatskele, Chatskele

Hey There, Chatskl

For those who are not at home in the Yiddish language, but who will want to sing the songs in the original, I would like to offer a bit of advice: Consult someone who knows the language and can transmit some of the subtleties of the song and its background to you. This is especially indicated in this type of song.

Wedding–dance song. English text by Ruth Rubin, ©1964 by Appleseed Music, Inc.

Chats - ke - le, Chats - ke - le, shpil mir a ka - zats - ke - le,
Hey, there, Chats - kl, Play it loud and bold __ We

Chotsh an o - ri - me, A - bi a chvats - ke.
may be poor __ but we've hearts of gold. __

O - rim iz nit gut, O - rim iz nit gut,
Pov - er - ty's a curse, Pov - er - ty's a curse.

Lo - mir zich nit she - men mit ey - ge - ne blut.
Lets not shame our re - la-tives that have an emp - ty purse.

Chatskele, chatskele, shpil mir a kazat-
  skele,
Chotsh an orime, abi a chvatske.

Refrain:

Orim iz nit gut,
Orim iz nit gut,
Lomir zich nit shemen
Mit eygene blut.

Nit kayn gebetene, aleyn gekumen,
Chotsh an orime, fort a mume.

Chatskele, chatskele, shpil mir a dume,
Chotsh an orime, abi a frume.

Hey there, Chatskl, play it loud and bold,
We may be poor, but we've hearts of
  gold.

Refrain:

Poverty's a curse,
Poverty's a curse,
Lets not shame the relatives
That have an empty purse.

The wedding invitation came to us
  belated,
We may be poor but we're still related.

Come now, Chatskl, play it loud and gay,
We are all Gods children on this wedding
  day.

Dremlen Feygl Oyf Di Tsvaygn

Sleep My Baby, Hungry Baby

The shooting of 4,000 Jewish men, women and children at Ponar (outside of Vilna, Lithuania) on April 5, 1943, left a grievous impression on the young poet, who herself, soon after, perished at the hands of the Nazis. A three-year-old child, wandering in the streets after the roundup moved the poet to write this lullaby. The melody may have been adapted from a song by the Soviet composer Polonsky.

Yiddish text by Leah Rudnitsky, (1916-1943). English text by Ruth Rubin, © 1964 by Appleseed Music, Inc.

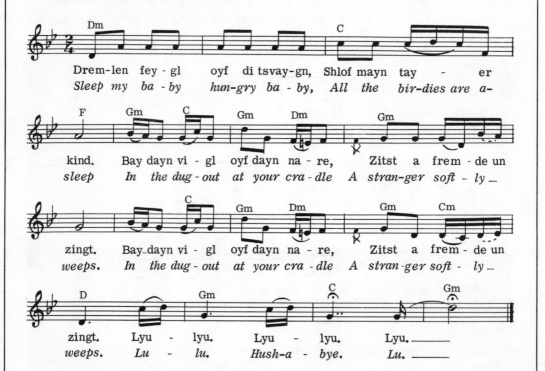

Drem-len fey-gl oyf di tsvay-gn, Shlof mayn tay - er kind.
Sleep my ba - by hun-gry ba - by, All the bir-dies are a-sleep

Bay dayn vi-gl oyf dayn na - re, Zitst a frem-de un zingt.
In the dug-out at your cra-dle A stran-ger soft-ly weeps.

Bay dayn vi-gl oyf dayn na - re, Zitst a frem-de un zingt.
In the dug-out at your cra-dle A stran-ger soft-ly weeps.

Lyu - lyu. Lyu - lyu. Lyu.
Lu - lu. Hush-a - bye. Lu.

Dremlen feygl oyf di tsvaygn,
Shlof mayn tayer kind,
Bay dayn vigl, oyf dayn nare,
Zitst a fremde un zingt:
　　Lyu-lyu, lyu-lyu, lyu.

S'iz dayn vigl vu geshtanen,
Oysgeflochtn fun glik.
Un dayn mame, oy dayn mame,
Kumt shoyn keynmol nit tsurik.
　　Lyu-lyu, lyu-lyu, lyu.

Sleep my baby, hungry baby,
All the birdies are asleep.
In the dugout, at your cradle,
A stranger softly weeps.
　　Lu-lu, lu-lu, lu.

You once had a home, my baby,
A mother and father as well.
Your mother was shot and died, in misery,
They stoned your father as he fell.
　　Lu-lu, lu-lu, lu.

Ch'ob gezen dayn tatn loyfn,
Unter hogl fun shteyn.
Iber felder iz gefloygn
Zayn faryosemter geveyn.
    Lyu-lyu, lyu-lyu, lyu.

Sleep my baby, hungry baby,
The moon is fast asleep.
In the dugout, at your cradle,
The stranger still softly weeps.
    Lu-lu, lu-lu, lu.

Du Meydele Du Fayns,
Du Meydele Du Sheyns

Pretty Little Girl, Can You Answer Me?

Riddle song. English text by Ruth Rubin, © 1964 by
Appleseed Music, Inc.

Du meydele du fayns, du meydele du sheyns,
Ich vel dir epes fregn, a retenish a kleyns:
-Vos iz hecher fun a hoyz?
 Un vos iz flinker fun amoyz?

Du narisher bocher, du narisher chlop!
Host doch nit kayn seychl in dayn kop!
-Der roych iz hecher fun a hoyz,
 A kats iz flinker fun a moyz.

Du meydele du fayns, du meydele du sheyns,
Ich vel dir epes fregn, a retenish a kleyns:
-Vos flit on fligl?
 Un vos moyert on tsigl?

Du narisher bocher, du narisher chlop!
Host doch nit kayn seychl in dayn kop!
-Der shney flit on fligl,
 Der frost moyert on tsigl.

Du meydele du fayns, du meydele du sheyns,
Ich vel dir epes fregn, a retenish a kleyns:
-Vos fara keyser iz on a land?
 Un vos fara vasser iz on zamd?

Du narisher bocher, du narisher chlop!
Host doch nit kayn seychl in dayn kop!
-Der keyser fun kortn hot nit kayn land,
 Trern fun di oygn zenen on zamd.

Pretty little girl, can you answer me?
Do you know the answers to my riddles, one, two, three?
-What can grow taller than a house?
 And what is swifter than a mouse?

Silly fellow you, you are stupid too,
There's not a brain inside your head, so let me answer you:
-Smoke rises taller than a house,
 A cat is swifter than a mouse.

Pretty little girl, can you answer me?
Do you know the answers to my riddles, one, two, three?
-What falls down and doesn't make a sound?
 Builds without bricks upon the bare ground?

Silly fellow you, you are stupid too,
There's not a brain inside your head, so let me answer you:
-Snow when it falls, doesn't make a sound,
 Frost needs no bricks to build upon the ground.

Pretty little girl, can you answer me?
Do you know the answers to my riddles, one, two, thre?
-Where is the king, without any land?
 And where is there water without a grain of sand?

Silly fellow you, you are stupid too,
There's not a brain inside your head, so let me answer you:
-The king of hearts, he hasn't any land,
 Tears from human eyes, haven't any sand.

29

Es Iz Gefloygn Di Gilderne Pave

The Golden Peacock Came A-Flying

In arranged marriages, the status of the groom's family rated higher, where the young husband was a scholar of the Torah. In these type songs, unhappy girls bewailed their fate, far from the tender love of parents, under the stern rule of a demanding mother-in-law.

English text by Ruth Rubin, © 1964 by Appleseed Music, Inc.

Es   iz ge-floy - gn di   gil-der-ne pa - ve,
The   gol-den pea - cock   came   a - fly - ing,

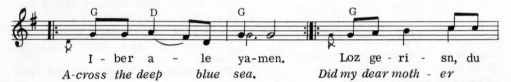

I - ber a - le ya-men.   Loz ge - ri - sn, du
A-cross the deep   blue sea.   Did my dear moth - er

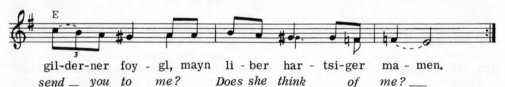

gil-der-ner foy - gl, mayn li - ber har - tsi-ger ma - men.
send __ you to   me?   Does she think   of   me? __

Es iz gefloygn, di gilderne pave,
Iber ale yamen.
Loz gerisn, du gilderner foygl,
Mayn liber, hartsiger mamen.

Gefloygn, gefloygn, di gilderne pave,
Ibern taych dem glatn -
Loz gerisn, du gilderner foygl,
Mayn libn, hartsign tatn.

Gefloygn, gefloygn, di gilderne pave,
Iber ale felder,
Hot zi farloyrn dem gildernem feder,
In di fremde lender.

Nit azoy di gilderne feder,
Vi di pave aleyn,
Nit azoy der fremder zun,
Vi di tochter aleyn.

The golden peacock came a-flying
Across the deep blue sea.
Did my dear mother send you to me?
Does she think of me?

The golden peacock came a-flying
From across the wide water.
Fly, oh bird, and tell my father
Of his lonely daughter.

The golden peacock flew and flew,
Over fields so bare.
In a distant land she dropped her
Golden feather there.

A flying peacock is a thing of beauty,
A golden plume is but a feather.
A son-in-law is often a stranger,
But a daughter is yours forever.

Vi es iz bitter, mayn libe muter,
A vasser on a fish.
Azoy iz bitter, mayn libe muter,
Bay a fremdn tish.

Vi es iz bitter, mayn libe muter,
A feygele on a nest,
Azoy iz bitter, mayn libe muter,
Shver un shviger's kest.

Sad it is, oh dearest mother,
For a fish to be without water,
So it is at a stranger's table
For your unhappy daughter.

Sad it is, oh dearest mother,
When a bird is torn from its nest.
So it is in the house of in-laws
As an uninvited guest.

Eyder Ich Leyg Mich Shlofn

No Sooner to Bed

Work song, (Seamstress apprentice.) English text by
Ruth Rubin, © 1964 by Appleseed Music, Inc.

Eyder ich leyg mich shlofn	No sooner to bed,
Darf ich shoyn oyfshteyn.	My bones full of pain,
Mit mayne kranke beyner	Then I must rise
Tsu der arbet geyn.	To work again.

Refrain:

Tsu got vel ich veynen	To the Lord I will weep,
Mit a groys geveyn.	To the Lord I will cry,
Vos ich bin geboyrn	Why was I born
A naytorn tsu zayn.	A seamstress, why?

Ch'kum shpet tsu der arbet	Should I come late,
S'iz doch vayt der veg,	I live so far away,
Shlogt men mir op	I am docked
Far halbe teg. (Ref.)	For a full half-day's pay. (Ref.)

Di nodlen vern tsubrochn	The needles are old,
Fuftsn a menut,	They constantly break.
Di finger vern tsushtochn,	My fingers, they bleed,
Es rint fun zey dos blut. (Ref.)	My God, how they ache! (Ref.)

Ich layd shtendig hunger	The boss makes me wait,
Ich hob nit vos tsu esn.	When I ask for my pay.
Vil ich gelt betn,	I've nothing to eat,
Heyst men mir fargesn. (Ref.)	I'm hungry all day. (Ref.)

IN COMPLIANCE WITH LAW?
The fire escape that ends in midair must be abolished.

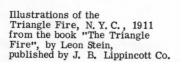

Illustrations of the
Triangle Fire, N. Y. C., 1911
from the book "The Triangle
Fire", by Leon Stein,
published by J. B. Lippincott Co.

Eyn Kol, Eyn Kol, Eyn Kol Vayn

Sparkling, Bubbling, Lovely Wine

This song is an "unfinished" song and the "D.C. Al Fine" is there for each singer to add his own verses....

Drinking song, collected by Ruth Rubin. English text by Ruth Rubin, © 1964 by Appleseed Music, Inc.

Eyn kol, eyn kol, eyn kol vayn. Eyn kol, eyn kol,
Spark - ling, bub - bling, love - ly wine, Spark-ling, bub - bling,

eyn kol vayn. Eyn kol, eyn kol, eyn kol vayn,
love - ly wine, Spark - ling, bub - bling, love - ly wine,

Ich ken on dir nit zayn. Eyn kol vayn, Ich
You make me feel so fine. Fine, fine, fine, You

kon on dir nit zayn. Eyn kol vayn, —— Ich
make me feel so fine, Spark - ling, bub-bling, love-ly wine, You

kon on dir nit zayn.
make me feel so fine.

Eyn kol, eyn kol, eyn kol vayn, (3x)
Ch'ken on dir nit zayn.

Eyn kol, eyn kol, eyn kol bir (3x)
Ch'ken nit zayn on dir.

Eyn kol, eyn kol, eyn kol yash (3x)
Ch'vil a fule flash.

Eyn kol, eyn kol, eyn kol konyak (3x)
Ay, iz dos geshmak!

Eyn kol, eyn kol, eyn kol kvas (3x)
Ch'vil a fule fas.

Sparkling, bubbling, lovely wine (3x)
You make me feel so fine.
Fine, fine, fine, you make me feel so
  fine,
Sparkling, bubbling, lovely wine,
You make me feel so fine.

Gurgling, foaming, frothy beer, (3x)
You fill me full of cheer.
Cheer, cheer, cheer, you fill me full of
  cheer,
Gurgling, foaming, frothy beer
You fill me full of cheer.

Good old whiskey, strong and free (3x)
A bottle is right for me.
Right for me; a bottle is right for me,
Good old whiskey, strong and free
A bottle is right for me.

Cognac isn't bad at all (3x)
It makes me grow so tall.
Tall, tall, tall; it makes me grow so
  tall,
Cognac isn't bad at all,
It makes me grow so tall.

If only cider is around (3x)
I'll drink that barrel down.
Down, down, down,
I'll drink that barrel down,
If only cider is around
I'll drink that barrel down.

Gibn Dir Mayn Tochter

Tell Me, Darling Daughter

Conversation song. English text by Ruth Rubin, © 1964 by Appleseed Music, Inc.

Gi-bn dir mayn toch-ter, Gi-bn dir mayn toch-ter, A
Tell me dar-ling daugh-ter, Tell me dar-ling daugh-ter, will you

shus-ter far a man? A shus-ter far a man? A
be a cob-bler's wife? Will you be a cob-bler's wife? A

shus-ter far a man vil ich nit, A shus-ter's a toch-ter
cob-bler's wife I will not be, Patch-ing old shoes is

bin ich nit La-ten shti-vl kon ich nit.
not for me, My fa-ther was no cob-bler No, not he!

Refrain

Zits ich oyf a shteyn, Un kuk a-rop un veyn, Un
I sit here on a stone, And weep and wail and moan,

ze vi a-le mey-de-lech ho-bn cha-se-ne, Un, nor ich blayb a-leyn.
All the young girls are get-ting mar-ried, And I am left a-lone.

Gibn dir mayn tochter, gibn dir mayn
  tochter,
A shuster far a man? A shuster far a
  man?
-A shuster far a man, vil ich nit,
  A shuster's a tochter, bin ich nit,
  Laten shtivl kon ich nit.

Tell me darling daughter, tell me
  darling daughter,
Will you be a cobbler's wife? Will you
  be a cobbler's wife?
-A cobbler's wife I will not be,
  Patching old shoes is not for me,
  My father was no cobbler, no, not he!

Refrain:

Zits ich oyf a shteyn,
Un kuk arop un veyn,
Un ze vi ale meydelech hobn chasene
Un nor ich blayb aleyn.

Gibn dir mayn tochter, gibn dir mayn
    tochter,
A shnayder far a man? A shnayder far
    a man?
-A shnayder far a man, vil ich nit,
 A shnayder's a tochter bin ich nit,
 Neyen kleyder kon ich nit.

    (Ref.)

Gibn dir mayn tochter, gibn dir mayn
    tochter,
A lamdn far a man? A lamdn far a man?
-A lamdn far a man, vil ich yo!
 A lamdn's a tochter, bin ich yo!
 Toyre lernen, kon ich yo.

Final Refrain:

Zits ich oyfn dach,
Un kuk arop un lach,
Un ze vi ale meydelech hobn chasene
Un ich bin mit zey glaych!

Refrain:

I sit here on a stone,
And weep and wail and moan,
All the young girls are getting married,
But I am left alone.

Tell me darling daughter, tell me
    darling daughter,
Will you be a tailor's wife? Will you be
    a tailor's wife?
-A tailor's wife I will not be,
 Stitching and sewing are not for me,
 My father was no tailor, no, not he!
 (Ref.)

Tell me darling daughter, tell me
    darling daughter,
Will you be a scholar's wife? Will you
    be a scholar's wife?
-A scholar's wife I'll gladly be,
 Studying the Torah is right for me,
 My father was a scholar, that was he!

Final Refrain:

Upon the roof sit I,
Laughing merrily,
Now I have found my own true mate,
And all may envy me!

Hob Ich a Por Oksn

Have You Seen My Honey Bears?

In translating a nonsense song, what can one do, but substitute one type of nonsense for another? - and still manage to keep something of the atmosphere of the original song!

Nonsense-cumulative. English text by Ruth Rubin.

Hob ich a por ok - sn, ok - sn, Vos zey bro-kn
Have you seen my hon-ey bears, hon - ey bears, Sit-ting up on

lok - shn, lok - shn, Ay — vun-der i - ber vun-der
wood-en chairs, wood - en chairs? Did you say, hon - ey bears,

vi di ok - sn bro - kn lok-shn. Dos iz mir a vun - der —
sit-ting up on wood-en chairs? Oh my dar-ling dear —————

Dos iz mir a vun - der.
Does-n't it seem queer?

Hob ich a por oksn, oksn,
Vos zey brokn lokshn, lokshn,
Ay, vunder iber vunder,
Vi di oksn brokn lokshn,

Refrain:

Dos iz mir a vunder!
Dos iz mir a vunder!

Hob ich a por bern, bern,
Vos zey shtiber, kern, kern,
Ay, vunder iber vunder,
Vi di bern shtiber kern,
Un di oksn brokn lokshn, (Ref.)

Have you seen my honey-bears, honey-bears,
Sitting up on wooden chairs,
    wooden chairs?
Did you say: honey-bears
Sitting up on wooden chairs?

Refrain:

Oh my darling dear,
Doesn't it seem queer?

Hob ich a por tsign, tsign,
Vos zey kinder vign, vign,
Ay vunder iber vunder,
Vi di tsign kinder vign,
Un di bern shtiber kern,
Un di oksn brokn lokshn, (Ref.)

Hob ich a por hint, hint,
Vos zey machn tint, tint,
Ay vunder iber vunder,
Vi di hint machn tint,
Un di tsign kinder vign,
Un di bern shtiber kern,
Un di oksn brokn lokshn, (Ref.)

Hob ich a por hener, hener,
Vos zey klaybn shpener, shpener.
Ay vunder iber vunder,
Vi di hener klaybn shpener,
Un di hint machn tint,
Un di tsign kinder vign,
Un di bern shtiber kern,
Un di oksn brokn lokshn, (Ref.)

Have you seen my pussy-cats, pussy-cats,
Dressed up in their fancy hats, fancy hats?
Did you say: pussy-cats
Dressed up in their fancy hats?
Honey-bears on wooden chairs? (Ref.)

Have you seen my woolly sheep, woolly sheep,
Rocking babies fast asleep, fast asleep,
Did you say: woolly sheep
Rocking babies fast asleep?
Pussy-cats in fancy hats,
Honey-bears on wooden chairs? (Ref.)

Have you seen my billy-goats, billy-goats,
Sailing down on river-boats, river-boats?
Did you say: billy-goats
Sailing down on river boats?
Woolly sheep fast asleep?
Pussy-cats in fancy hats?
Honey-bears on wooden chairs? (Ref.)

Hop, Mayne Homentashn!

Hey, Hey, Homentashn!

Purim song. English lyrics by Ruth Rubin, © 1964 by Appleseed Music, Inc.

Yachne-Dvoshe fort in mark,
Zi halt zich in eyn pakn,
Fort oyf purim koyfn mel,
Homntashn bakn.

Refrain:

Hop, mayne homntashn,
Hop, mayne vayse!
Hop, mit mayne homntashn
Hot pasirt a mayse!

S'geyt a regn, s'geyt ashney,
S'kapet fun di decher,
Yachne firt shoyn kornmel,
In a zak mit lecher.

I'll tell you of a pretty girl,
Who was always in a flurry,
She baked her Purim homentashn,
In an awful hurry.

Refrain:

Hey, hey, you homentashn,
You might have been so tasty-
But you were the victims of
A pretty girl so hasty!

That girl, she hurried off to town,
Shaking with her bustle,
To buy the flour and poppy-seed,
As fast as she could hustle.

Nit kayn honig, nit kayn mon,
Un fargesn heyvn,
Yachne macht shoyn homntashn,
S'bakt zich shoyn in oyvn.

Yachne firt shoyn shalach-mones,
Tsu der bobe yente,
Tsvey-dray homntashn,
Halb-roy, halb farbrente.

She forgot the salt, forgot the yeast,
It wasn't even funny -
The flour was in a sorry mess,
But her heart was sweet as honey.

Our maid then baked the homentashn,
But half were raw and pasty,
The other was burnt quite to a crisp,
The mess was far from tasty!

Hot Zich Mir Di Zip Tsezipt

My Old Sieve Was All Worn Out

About 20 years ago, when I first collected this Yiddish folksong from my Mother, she could not remember more than the first stanza! I was heartbroken. But in time, like most "carriers", I added two additional stanzas, which I sang and recorded time and again. But this is the first time I have confessed to having authored them!....

Dancing song. English text by Ruth Rubin, © 1964 by Appleseed Music, Inc.

Hot zich mir di zip tse-zipt un hot zich mir tsu-bro-chn,
My old sieve was all worn out, to - day it broke in two.

Hot zich mir di shich tse-ri-sn, tants ich in di hoy-le zo-kn.
Danc-ing in your stock-ing feet is bet - ter than in shoes.

Tants, tants ant-ke-gn mir, Un ich ant-ke-gn dir,
I will dance with you my dear, and you will dance with me,

Du vest nemen dem ey - dim, un ich vel nemen di shnir!
You can have the son in law, The daugh-ter-in - law's for me!

Hot zich mir di zip tsezipt	My old sieve was all worn out,
Un hot zich mir tsebrochn.	Today it broke in two-
Hot zich mir di shich tserisn	Dancing in your stocking-feet
Tants ich in di hoyle zokn!	Is better than in shoes!
Refrain:	Refrain:
Tants, tants antkegn mir,	I will dance with you, my dear,
Un ich antkegn dir -	And you will dance with me.
Du vest nemen dem eydim	You can have the son-in-law,
Un ich vel nemen di shnir!	The daughter-in-law's for me!

Tsebrochn iz der lokshntop,
Farbrent der nahit -
Tantsn di machteynestes,
Di kale in der mit.

Chosn's tsad un kale's tsad -
Di gantse mishpoche -
Tantsn oyf der chasene
In mazl un in broche!

Broken is my noodle-pot
The chickpeas burned inside.
All the ladies now are dancing
Round and round the bride.

Everybody's come to dance
And eat and drink right hearty,
Rich and poor and old and young
Have come to the wedding party!

Lomir Zich Iberbetn

Come, Let's Be Friends Again

Wedding dance folksong. English text by Ruth Rubin,
© 1964 by Appleseed Music, Inc.

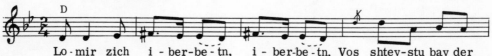

Lo-mir zich i-ber-be-tn, i-ber-be-tn, Vos shtey-stu bay der
Come, lets be friends a-gain,— friends a-gain,— Don't stand there at the

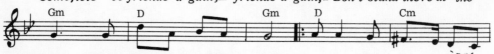

tir? Vos shtey-stu bay der tir? Lo-mir zich i-ber-be-tn,
door. Don't stand there at the door. Come, lets be friends a-gain,—

kum a-rayn tsu mir. mir.
friends for ev-er-more. more.

Lomir zich iberbetn, iberbetn,	Come, lets be friends again, friends again,
Vos shteystu bay der tir?	Don't stand there at the door.
Lomir zich iberbetn,	Come lets be friends again,
Kum arayn tsu mir.	Friends for evermore.
Lomir zich iberbetn, iberbetn,	Come, lets be friends again, friends again,
Vos shteystu bay mayn fenster?	Don't hide behind the wall.
Lomir zich iberbetn,	Come, lets be friends again,
Bist bay mir der shenster.	I love you best of all.
Lomir zich iberbetn, iberbetn,	Come, lets be friends again, friends again,
Koyf a por marantsn,	We're birds of a feather.
Lomir zich iberbetn,	Come, lets be friends again,
Lomir geyen tantsn.	And dance about together.
Lomir zich iberbetn, iberbetn,	Come, lets be friends again, friends again,
Shtel dem samovar,	I'll put up the tea.
Lomir zich iberbetn,	Come, lets be friends again,
Zay-zhe nisht kayn nar.	Come and sit by me.
Lomir zich iberbetn, iberbetn,	Come lets be friends again, friends again,
Lomir nisht zayn vi geyrim,	We will help each other,
Lomir zich iberbetn,	Come lets be friends again,
Lomir zayn chaverım	I will be your brother.

Gey Ich Mir Shpatsirn

I Strolled Out One Spring Morning

Obviously of German origin. To keep the spirit of this saucy song, I have added an extra verse to the English translation.

Flirtation song, collected by Ruth Rubin. English text by Ruth Rubin, © 1964 by Appleseed Music, Inc.

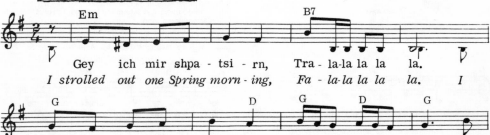

Gey ich mir shpa-tsi-rn, Tra-la-la la la la.
I strolled out one Spring morn-ing, Fa-la-la la la la. I

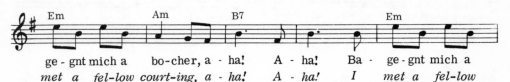

Gey ich mir shpa-tsi-rn, Tra-la-la la la la la. Ba-
strolled out one Spring morn-ing, Fa-la-la la la la la. I

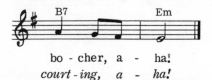

ge-gnt mich a bo-cher, a - ha! A - ha! Ba- ge-gnt mich a
met a fel-low court-ing, a - ha! A - ha! I met a fel-low

bo - cher, a - ha!
court-ing, a - ha!

Gey ich mir shpatsirn, tralala lalala.
Gey ich mir shpatsirn, tralala lalala, la.
Bagegnt mich a bocher, aha! (2)

Er zogt er vet mich nemen, tralala etc.
Er leygt es op oyf vinter, aha, aha.

Der vinter iz gekumen, etc.
Er hot mich nit genumen, etc.

Itst vil er mich shoyn nemen, etc.
Ober ich vil im nit kenen, aha, aha!

I strolled out one Spring morning, falala lalala,
I strolled out one Spring morning, falala, lalala, la.
I met a fellow courting, aha, aha! (2)

He said some day we'll marry, etc.
But now, he could not tarry, aha, aha!

The seasons passed me by, etc.
That fellow made me sigh, aha, aha!

Another fair Spring morning, etc.
That fellow came a-courting, aha, aha!

But all the while he tarried, etc.
Oh, I was safely married, aha, aha!

Mayn Yingele

My Little Son

This cradle song, of a sweatshop worker, was written in New York City in 1887, by Morris Rosenfeld. It was a time when the mass migrations of Jews from Eastern Europe were in full swing. Rosenfeld's poetry became very popular and a number of his poems were set to music by anonymous composers. His sung poems came to be known to Yiddish-speaking people on both sides of the Atlantic, and subsequently, wherever Yiddish was spoken. The two musical variants to Mayn Yingele given here, attest to this. Rosenfeld's poetry was also translated into English and then into a number of European languages (thanks to Leo Wiener, Professor of Literature at Harvard University at that time), which made him world renowned. Mayn Yingele too, has been translated many times, and into many tongues. Several English translations were made.

Text by Morris Rosenfeld, tune anonymous. English text by Ruth Rubin, © 1964 by Appleseed Music, Inc.

Ich hob a kley-nem yin-ge-le, A zu-ne-le gor fayn. Ven
I have a hand-some ba-by son, A lit-tle boy so fine. And

ich der-ze im dacht zich mir, Di gan-tse velt iz mayn. Nor
when I look at him I feel, The whole wide world is mine. But

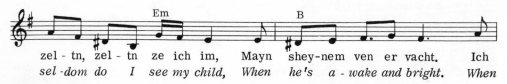

zel-tn, zel-tn ze ich im, Mayn shey-nem ven er vacht. Ich
sel-dom do I see my child, When he's a-wake and bright. When

tref im i-mer shlof-n-dig, Ich ze im nor bay nacht.
I leave home he's fast a-sleep, When I re-turn its night.

Ich hob a kleynem yingele	I have a handsome baby son,
A zunele gor fayn.	A little boy, so fine.
Ven ich derze im, dacht zich mir,	And when I look at him, I feel
Di gantse velt iz mayn.	The whole wide world is mine.
Nor zeltn, zeltn, ze ich im,	But seldom do I see my child,
Mayn sheynem, ven er vacht.	When he's awake and bright,
Ich tref im imer shlofndig,	When I leave home, he's still asleep,
Ich ze im nor baynacht.	When I return, its night.
Di arbet traybt mich fri aroys,	To toil, I'm driven out at dawn,
Un lozt mich shpet tsurik.	Its dark when I return.
O fremd iz mir mayn eygn layb,	I seem a stranger to myself,
O, fremd, mayn kind's a blik.	Estranged from those I yearn.

Ich kum tsuklemterheyt aheym,
In finsternish gehilt,
Mayn bleyche froy dertseylt mir bald
Vi fayn dos kind zich shpilt.

Vi zis es redt, vi klug es fregt:
O Mame, gute Ma,
Ven kumt un brengt a pene mir,
Mayn guter, guter Pa?"

Ich her es tsu, un yo, es muz,
Yo, yo, es muz geshen!
Di foter-libe flakert oyf,
Es muz mayn kind mich zen!

Ich shtey bay zayn gelegerl,
Un ze un her un sha;
A troym bavegt di lipelech:
"O, vu iz, vu iz Pa"

Ich kush di bloye oygelech,
Zey efenen zich, O kind!
Zey ze-en mich, zey ze-en mich!
Un shlisn zich geshvind.

Do shteyt dayn Papa tayerer,
A penele dir, na!
A troym bavegt di lipelech;
O vu iz, vu iz Pa?

Ich blayb tsuveytogt un tsuklemt,
Farbitert, un ich kler:
Ven du ervachst amol, mayn kind,
Gefinstu mich nit mer...

When I come home so wearily,
My wife describes the day -
How happily our child does romp,
The bright things he does say.

How wistfully he says to her:
Where can my Daddy be?
Will he come and bring some day
A penny, all for me?

I listen sadly to her tale,
My wasted life I rue -
I want to see my child again!
For him to know me too...

I stand beside the little crib,
And watch my sleeping son.
In his dreams he's whispering;
Where has my Daddy gone?

I gaze at him and kiss his eyes,
They seem to look at me!
But then they close, he's fast asleep-
Still whispering dreamily.

Your Daddy's brought your penny, son,
I kiss his tender brow.
The dream still whispers from his lips:
Where is my Daddy now?

I look at him in anguish then,
I know - it seems so clear -
When once again, my child awakes -
His Daddy won't be here.....

Variant Melody

Ich hob a kley-nem yin-ge-le, A zu-ne-le gor fayn.__ Ven
I have a hand-some ba-by son. A lit-tle boy so fine.__ And

ich der-ze im dacht zich mir, Di gan-tse velt iz mayn.__ Nor
when I look at him I feel, the whole wide world is mine. __ But

zel-tn, zel-tn ze ich im, Mayn shey-nem ven__er vacht.__ Ich
sel-dom do I see my child, when he's a-wake and bright. When

tref im i-mer shlof-n-dig, Ich ze im nor bay nacht.__
I leave home he's fast a-sleep, When I re-turn it's night.___

Michalku

Children's song. English text by Ruth Rubin, ©1964 by Appleseed Music, Inc.

Hob ich mir a kley-nem Mi-chal-ku, Mi-chal-ku,
I have a ver-y good friend Mi-chal-ku, Mi-chal-ku,

Voynt er oyf der lang - er gas. Macht er mir
He does-n't live so ver-y far a - way. He makes for me what-

vos er ken Macht er mir vos er vil, Macht er mir a
ev - er I wish, he makes for me what - ev-er he can, Once he made a

pay - ke - le, Dos pay - ke - le macht a - zoy: Ta-ra -
lit-tle round drum, The lit-tle drum went ta-ra - boom! Ta-ra -

bam-bam- bam, Ta-ra-bam-bam - bam. A - zoy macht dos
boom-boom - boom, Ta-ra -boom-boom-boom, — Lis-ten to the lit-tle round

pay - ke - le.
drum.

Refrain:

Hob ich mir a kleynem Michalku,
  Michalku,
Voynt er oyf der langer gas.
Macht er mir vos er vil,
Macht er mir vos er ken:

Refrain:

I have a very good friend Michalku,
  Michalku,
He doesn't live so very far away.
He makes for me whatever I wish,
He makes for me whatever he can:

Macht er mir a paykele,
Dos paykele macht azoy:
Tarabambambam, Tarabambambam,
Azoy macht dos paykele! (Ref.)

Macht er mir a fayfele,
Dos fayfele macht azoy:
Flufluflu, flufluflu,
Azoy macht dos fayfele! (Ref.)

Macht er mir a fidele,
Dos fidele macht azoy:
Fidldidldidl, fidldidldidl,
Azoy macht dos fidele. (Ref.)

Macht er mir a trubetske,
Di trubetske macht azoy:
Trutrutru, trutrutru,
Azoy macht di trubetske. (Ref.)

Macht er mir a tsimbele,
Dos tsimbele macht azoy:
Tsimtsimtsim, tsimtsimtsim,
Azoy macht dos tsimbele. (Ref.)

Once he made a little round rum,
The little drum went: Taraboom!
Taraboomboomboom, Taraboomboom-
   boom,
Listen to the little round drum. (Ref.)

Then he made a whistle too,
This is how the whistle blew:
Flufluflufle, flufluflu,
This is how the whistle blew! (Ref.)

One fine day he made for me,
the tiniest little fiddle-dee-dee,
Feedl-deedl-deedl, dee-dee-dee,
The nicest little fiddle for me! (Ref.)

He made a bugle for me too,
This is how the bugle blew:
Trutrutrutru, trutrutru,
This is how the bugle blew! (Ref.)

A triangle he made so small,
And said that that was really all.
It made a little tsimtsimtsim -
But that was absolutely all. (Ref.)

Ot Azoy Neyt A Shnayder

This Is How a Tailor Stitches

A work song of the beginning of the 19th century, acquires two additional stanzas (3 and 4), towards the end of the 80s, when the struggle for the ten hour day, was crowned with success, in a particular strike.

English text by Ruth Rubin, © 1964 by Appleseed Music, Inc.

Refrain:
Ot a-zoy neyt a shnay-der, Ot a-zoy neyt er doch.
This is how a tai-lor stitch-es, This is how he sews and sews.

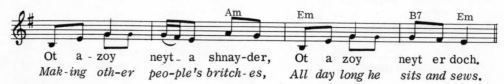

Ot a-zoy neyt a shnay-der, Ot a zoy neyt er doch.
Mak-ing oth-er peo-ple's britch-es, All day long he sits and sews.

Er neyt un neyt a gant-se voch, far-dint a gil-dn mit a loch.
A tai-lor works hard all the time and all he gets is a lou-sy dime.

Refrain:

Ot azoy neyt a shnayder,
Ot azoy neyt er doch.
Ot azoy neyt a shnayder,
Ot azoy neyt er doch.

Er neyt un neyt a gantse voch,
Fardint a gildn mit a loch.

A shnayder neyt un neyt un neyt,
Fardint kadoches, nit kayn broyt.

Farayorn, nit haynt gedacht,
Hobn mir gehorevet fun acht biz acht.

Ober di struktsye hot gemacht,
Mir horeven shoyn mer nit fun acht biz
   acht.

Refrain:

This is how a tailor stitches,
This is how he sews and sews,
Making other people's britches,
All day long he sits and sews.

A tailor works hard all the time,
But all he gets is a lousy dime.

A tailor sews to earn his bread,
And gets the misery instead.

A year ago we worked till late,
Twelve long hours, from eight to eight.

But now the union's set us straight,
We work no more from eight to eight.

The tailor boss is in a fix,
We only work from eight to six.

Oyfn Barg Un Ibern Barg

Up the Hill and Over the Hill

English text by Ruth Rubin, © 1964 by Appleseed Music, Inc.

Oy - fn barg un — i - ber-n barg —— fli - en toy - bn po - rn. Noch kayn na - ches nit der-lebt, shoyn a - vek di yo - rn. yo - rn.

Up the hill and — over the hill —— ma - ting doves do fly. —— Our young joys have come and gone, Life has passed us by. —— by.

Oyfn barg un ibern barg
Flien toybn porn.
Noch kayn naches nit derlebt,
Shoyn avek di yorn.

Lomir shpanen ferd un vogn,
Lomir loyfn, forn,
Efsher veln mir deryogn
Undzere yunge yorn.

Shoyn deryogt di yunge yorn
Oyfn hoychn brik.
Yorn, yorn, kert zich um,
Chotsh in gest tsurik!

Neyn, mir veln zich nit umkern,
S'iz nito tsu vemen!
Hot ir frier nit bedarft
Undz azoy farshemen!

Up the hill and over the hill
Mating doves do fly.
Our young joys have come and gone,
Life has passed us by.

Let us harness horse to wagon,
Let us quickly fly.
Let us overtake our youth
That has passed us by.

We caught up with our fair youth
At highbridge on the plain,
Return sweet years of long ago
Be our guests again!

No, no, no, we can't come back,
You're all old to-day.
You should not have, long ago,
Wasted us away...

Oy, A Nacht A Sheyne

The Moon Was Sailing in the Sky

Two lovers, faced with separation, decide to marry before he goes into the army.

English text by Ruth Rubin, © 1964 by Appleseed Music, Inc. (Last stanza collected by Ruth Rubin, 1964.)

Oy a nacht a shey - ne, __ Di nacht iz ge-ven a -zoy
The moon was sail - ing in the sky. __ The night was so soft and so

sheyn. __ Di sheyn. __ Af a ben - ke - le ze-nen mir ge - ze - sn, __ Di le-
blue. __ The blue. __ On a bench with our arms round each oth - er __ We

vo-ne hot ge - nu-men a - vek - geyn. __ af a geyn.
sat there the whole __ night through. __ On a through.

Oy, a nacht a sheyne,
Di nacht iz geven azoy sheyn.
Oyf a benkele zenen mir gezesn,
Di levone hot genumen avekgeyn.

Oyf a benkele zenen mir gezesn,
Un hobn tsuzamen farbracht.
Vifil reyd mir hobn ayngetaynet,
Tsu kayn tolk hobn mir zich nit der-
    tracht.

Vos-zhe fara tolk libe, vilstu?
Az ich muz tsu dem priziv shteyn.
Kayn knasmol kenen mir nit machn,
Dos kenstu doch aleyn farshteyn.

Oyf banen vel ich forn,
Un oyf vasern shvimen tsu dir.
Ch'vel farlozn foter un muter,
Un kumen, zis-lebn tsu dir.

The moon was sailing in the sky
The night was so soft and so blue.
On a bench with our arms round each
    other,
We sat there the whole night through.

Oh, we talked for many long hours,
But what was there more we could say?
I had to go into the army,
I had to leave home the next day.

How can I marry you now, my dear,
Yet how can I leave you alone?
I know that you'll wait for me faithfully,
When in three years from now, I'll
    come home.

(She:)
I will ride the trains, oh my darling,
And sail over waters so blue.
I will leave both my father and mother,
Just to be, my own true love, with you.

Oyf kayn banen zolsu nit
  forn,
Un oyf vasern nit shvimen tsu
  mir.
A chupe, oy dushenyu, lomir
  shteln,
Un in dray yor vel ich kumen tsu dir!

(He:)
Don't you ride the trains, oh my darling,
And don't sail the waters so blue.
Tomorrow, I'll marry you, my own
  true love,
And in three years, I'll come back to
  you!

Oy, Dortn, Dortn, Ibern Vasserl

Away across the Hills

Love song. English lyrics by Ruth Rubin, © 1964 by
Appleseed Music, Inc.

Oy, dor-tn, dor - tn i-bern vas - - ser - l, Oy,
A - way a-cross the hills, and a - way a-cross the fields, A -

dor - tn, dor - tn, i - ber-n brik, _____ Far -
way a-cross the sea wide_ and _ blue, _____ I have

tri - bn hos-tu mich, in di vay - te-ne len - der, Un
gone and left you, love, in the land_ of _ me-mo - ry, And

ben - ken, benk ich noch dir tsu - rik.
sit here dream-ing now, my sweet, of you.

Oy, dortn, dortn, ibern vasserl,
Oy, dortn, dortn, ibern brik.
Fartribn hostu mich in di vaytene lender,
Un benken, benk ich noch dir tsurik.

Oy, vifil ovntlech, tsuzamen gezesn,
Oy, vifil ovntlech, shpet in der nacht.
Oy, vivil trerelech, mir hobn fargosn,
Oy, biz mir hobn di libe tsuzamenge-
    bracht.

Away across the hills and away across
    the fields,
Away across the sea, wide and blue.
I have gone and left you, love, in the land
    of memory,
And sit here dreaming, now, my sweet,
    of you.

I recall the gentle hours, the moonlit
    lovely hours,
When we promised all the love within
    our heart.
When we planned our life as one, for
    the happy years to come,
And now we're yearning, miles and
    miles apart.

Oy, dayne oygelech, vi di shvartse karshelech,
Un dayne lipelech vi rozeve papir.
Un dayne fingerlech, vi tint un vi feder,
Oy, shraybn zolstu ofte briv tsu mir.

I recall your eyes so black, like the cherries dark and ripe,
Your lips so pink, so soft and oh, so sweet.
I recall your slender hands and your fingers long and slim,
Oh Lord, I pray that once again we'll meet.

Oyfn Pripetshok

On the Little Hearth

This cradle song was written in the Czarist Pale of Settlement, where trials and tribulations were the natural environment of the Jewish Community. It was on the eve of the mass migrations to America and the lullaby actually anticipates the "exodus".

Mark Warshawsky authored more than fifty-texts and tunes, many of which were current among the people before they were published. Oyfn Pripetshok, however, became the most popular of his songs, and is known wherever Yiddish-speaking Jews reside the world over.

Text and Tune by Mark Warshawsky (1848-1907). English text by Ruth Rubin, ©1964 by Appleseed Music, Inc.

Oy - fn pri - pe - tshok   brent a fay - er - l,   Un   in shtub iz
On the lit - tle hearth, A fire is burn-ing bright, The school-room is   so

heys.   Un - der re - be ler - nt   kley - ne kin - der-lech,
warm.   The old teach-er's tell - ing   all   the child-ren there, How the

Dem — a - leph   beys   Dem — a - leph   beys.
al-pha-bet   was   born.   al-pha-bet   was   born.

Refrain

Zet-zhe kin-der-lech Ge-denkt-zhe tay - e - re,   Vos ir lern - t
Lis-ten chil - dren Lis - ten pre-cious ones, Lis - ten to   our

do.   Zogt-zhe noch a - mol un   ta - ke noch a - mol,
love.   But first you have to read the   an-cient al - pha-bet,

Ko - mets a - leph,   O.   Ko - mets a - leph   O!
Be-fore you can   learn   more.   Be-fore you can   learn   more.

Oyfn pripetshok brent a fayerl,
Un in shtub iz heys.
Un der rebe lernt kleyne kinderlech
Dem alef-beys.

Refrain:

Zet-zhe kinderlech, gedenkt-zhe
    tayere,
Vos ir lernt do;
Zogt-zhe noch amol, un take noch amol:
Komets-alef: O!

Lernt kinder, mit groys cheyshek,
Azoy zog ich aych on,
Ver s'vet gicher fun aych kenen ivre,
Der bakumt a fon. (Ref.)

Lernt kinder, hot nit moyre,
Yeder onhoyb iz shver,
Gliklech der vos hot gelernt toyre,
Tsi darf der mentsh noch mer? (Ref.)

Ir vet kinder, elter vern,
Vet ir aleyn farshteyn,
Vifil in di oysyes lign trern,
Un vifil geveyn. (Ref.)

Az ir vet kinder, dem goles shlepn,
Oysgemutshet zayn,
Zolt ir fun di oysyes koyech shepn,
Kukt in zey arayn! (Ref.)

On the little hearth a fire is burning
    bright,
The schoolroom is so warm -
The old teacher's telling all the children
    there,
How the alphabet was born.

Refrain:

Listen children, listen precious ones,
Listen to our lore,
But first you have to read the ancient
    alphabet
Before you can learn more.

It will lead you to the holy books,
Remember what I say -
Then I'll give a banner to the best of you,
On the holiday. (Ref.)

Pay attention, children listen well,
Its always hard to start -
Happy is the man who lives with knowl-
    edge,
Takes learning to his heart. (Ref.)

When you'll grow up into men some day,
Then you'll surely know,
How full of human tears is our old
    alphabet,
How full of trials and woe. (Ref.)

And if one day, we should be driven out
From this land of pain -
May you seek and find in our old alphabet
The strength to build again. (Ref.)

Papir Iz Doch Vays

One Day As I Was Walking

Love song. English lyrics by Ruth Rubin. ©1964 by Appleseed Music, Inc.

Pa - pir iz doch vays __ un tint __ iz doch shvarts. Tsu
One day as I was walk - ing __ down the bus - y street.

dir mayn zis le - bn, tsit __ doch mayn harts. Ich volt
Man-y pret - ty maid - ens I hap-pened to meet. But there

shten - dig ge - ze - sn dray teg __ noch - an - and, Tsu
wasn't __ one a - mong them that could at all com - pare, With my

ku-shn dayn sheyn __ po - nim un tsu hal - tn dayn hant.
true love's bright __ smile and her love - ly black hair.

Papir iz doch vays un tint iz doch shvarts,
Tsu dir mayn zis lebn, tsit doch mayn harts.
Ich volt shtendig gezesn, dray teg nochanand,
Tsu kushn dayn sheyn ponim un tsu haltn dayn hant.

Nechtn bin ich oyf a chasene geven,
Fil sheyne meydelech hob ich dort gezen.
Ay, fil sheyne meydelech, tsu dir kumt nit gor,
Mit dayne shvartse eygelech un mit dayne shvartse hor.

One day as I was walking down the busy street,
Many pretty maidens I happened to meet.
But there wasn't one among them that could at all compare,
With my true love's bright smile and her lovely black hair.

My darling is charming and gentle are her ways,
She has bound me with tenderness, forever and always.
My thoughts of her have filled me with purest delight,
I think of her all the day and I dream of her at night.

58

Ach du liber Got, her oys mayn
farlang,
Dem oysher gistu kovid, mit a sheynem
gang,
Oy, mir gib a shtibele oyf dem groz
dem grinem,
Az ich mit mayn zis-lebn zoln voynen
derinen.

On a hill in a mansion live the rich
of our town,
They are laden with money, comfort
and renown.
All I want is just one thing, it seems
simple to me -
A little hut in the greenwood for my
darling and me.

Shlof Mayn Kind, Mayn Treyst, Mayn Sheyner

Sleep My Baby, My Sweet Comfort

One of the most popular songs of the mass migration years of East European Jews to America, this lullaby was circulating among the people in Eastern Europe, in several textual and musical variants, even before it was published by Sholem Aleichem in Odessa, in 1892. Two versions are given here: the 1892 D. Kovanovski version and an anonymous version, transcribed by Ruth Rubin. Both are still current here.

Yiddish text by Sholem Aleichem. Melody based on a tune by D. Kovanovski. English Text by Ruth Rubin, © 1964 by Appleseed Music, Inc.

Shlof mayn kind, mayn treyst mayn shey-ner, Shlof-zhe zu-ne-nyu,
Sleep my ba-by, My sweet com-fort, Sleep my love-ly son.

Shlof mayn kind, mayn ka-dish ey-ner, Shlof-zhe, lyu, lyu,— lyu.
Hush, my child, my pre-cious dar-ling, Hush, my lit-tle — one.

Shlof mayn kind, mayn ka-dish ey-ner, Shlof-zhe lyu, lyu,— lyu.
Hush, my child, my pre-cious dar-ling, Hush, my lit-tle — one.

Shlof mayn kind, mayn treyst, mayn
sheyner,
Shlof-zhe zunenyu,
Shlof mayn kind, mayn kadish eyner,
Shlof-zhe, lyu-lyu-lyu.

Bay dayn vigl zitst dayn mame,
Zingt a lid un veynt.
Vest amol farshteyn mistame,
Vos zi hot gemeynt.

In amerike iz der tate,
Dayner, zunenyu,
Du bizt noch a kind, lesate,
Shlof-zhe, lyu-lyu-lyu.

Sleep my baby, my sweet comfort,
Sleep my lovely son.
Hush my child, my precious darling,
Hush, my little one.

Mother sits beside your cradle
Crooning tearfully.
Some day, you will understand
What these tears mean to me.

Your daddy's in America
A thousand miles away,
You are still a tiny baby,
What more can I say?

In amerike iz far yedn,
Zogt men, gor a glik.
Un far yedn a gan-eydn,
Gor epes an antik.

America, the people tell me,
Brings good luck to all.
Everybody lives in comfort,
In houses very tall.

Dortn est men in der vochn,
Chale, zunenyu,
Yaychelech vel ich dir kochn,
Shlof-zhe, lyu-lyu-lyu.

In the weekdays, so they tell me,
They eat white bread, son,
Chicken broth, I'll make for you there,
Sleep now, little one.

Er vet shikn tsvantsig doler,
Zayn portret dertsu,
Un vet nemen, lebn zol er,
Undz ahintsutsu.

Twenty dollars and his picture,
Daddy'll send us here.
And we'll sail across the water,
To join him there, my dear.

Er vet chapn undz un kushn,
Tantsn azh far freyd,
Ich vel kvaln trern gisn,
Veynen shtilerheyt.

He will put his arms around us,
Kiss us joyfully.
I will be so happy, darling,
Weeping silently.

Biz es kumt dos gute kvitl,
Shlof-zhe zunenyu,
Shlofn iz a tayer mitl,
Shlof-zhe, lyu-lyu-lyu.

Till that blessed moment comes,
The days are sad and long.
Sleep is such a soothing comfort,
Sleep my son, grow strong.

Shlof Mayne Kind, Mayn Treyst, Mayn Sheyner
(version II)

Yiddish folk lullaby. English text by Ruth Rubin, ©1964
by Appleseed Music, Inc.

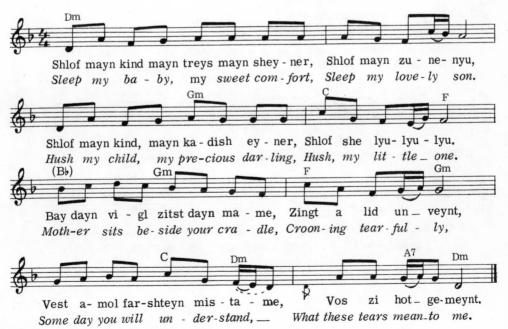

Shlof mayn kind mayn treys mayn shey-ner, Shlof mayn zu-ne-nyu,
Sleep my ba-by, my sweet com-fort, Sleep my love-ly son.

Shlof mayn kind, mayn ka-dish ey-ner, Shlof she lyu-lyu-lyu.
Hush my child, my pre-cious dar-ling, Hush, my lit-tle one.

Bay dayn vi-gl zitst dayn ma-me, Zingt a lid un veynt,
Moth-er sits be-side your cra-dle, Croon-ing tear-ful-ly,

Vest a-mol far-shteyn mis-ta-me, Vos zi hot ge-meynt.
Some day you will un-der-stand, — What these tears mean to me.

Shpilt-zhe Mir Dem Nayem Sher

Play That Lovely Tune for Me

A Sher is a traditional 19th century Jewish group dance.

English text by Ruth Rubin, ©1964 by Appleseed Music, Inc.

Shpilt-zhe mir dem nay - em sher, Vos iz a - roys - ge - ku - men,
Play that love - ly tune for me, The Sher that they're all danc - ing,

Ich hob zich far-libt in a yin-ge-le a shey-nem, Un kon tsu im nit ku - men.
I'm in love with a hand - some lad, But I dare not go ro - manc-ing.

Ch'volt tsu im ge-ku - men, Voynt er - zey - er vayt.
I would love to see him, But he lives - far a - way.

Ch'volt doch im a kush ge-ge-bn, Shem ich zich far - layt.
I would love to kiss him, But what would peo-ple - say?

Nit a - zoy far layt, _____ Vi far Gott a - leyn,
Its not so much the folks, But its the Lord I fear,

Ch'volt mit im far-bracht di tsayt az key-ner zol nit zen!
Oh, I would love to be with him, When no one else is near!

Refrain:

Shpilt-zhe mir dem nayem sher
Vos iz aroysgekumen,
Ich hob zich farlibt in a yingele a
   sheynem
Un kon tsu im nit kumen.

Ch'volt tsu im gekumen,
Voynt er zeyer vayt,
Ch'volt doch im a kush gegebn,
Shem ich zich far layt!
Nit azoy far layt,
Vi far Gott aleyn,
Ch'volt mit im farbracht di tsayt,
Az keyner zol nit zen! (Ref.)

Kum-zhe tsu mir gicher,
Ich vart oyf dir shoyn lang.
Kum-zhe gich ariber,
Men zol nit hern dayn gang.
Fir ich dich in shtibele,
Fun mayn mame'n aleyn,
Chosn-kale veln mir zayn
Un tsu der chupe geyn! (Ref.)

Refrain:

Play that lovely tune for me
The Sher that they're all dancing.
I'm in love with a handsome lad
But I dare not go romancing -

I would love to see him
But he lives far away.
I would love to kiss him -
But what will people say?
Its not so much the folks
But its the Lord I fear -
Oh, I would love to be with him
When no one else is near. (Ref.)

Come, my love, come softly,
Come quickly, I implore -
Let nobody see you, darling,
Coming to my door -
Come into my home -
And meet my family,
They will bless us both, my love,
And married we will be! (Ref.)

Shvartse Karshelech Raysn Mir

Red Cherries Are Not for Picking

Dancing song, Waltz. English text by Ruth Rubin,
©1964 by Appleseed Music, Inc.

Shvar - tse kar-she-lech ray-sn mir, — Roy - te lo - zn mir
Red cher-ries are not for pick - ing, — On - ly the black ones are

shteyn, — Shey - ne mey-de-lech ne-men mir, —
sweet, — We al-ways choose the pret-ty girls, — They are

Mi - se lo - zn mir geyn, Eyns-tsvey, eyns-tsvey-dray
nim - ble and fast on their feet, one - two, one - two-three,

Oy, vey iz tsu mir, — Vey iz tsu may - ne
Oh, woe is to me, — Woe is to me — I

yor, — A li - be hob ich ge - firt, — A
say, — I fell so deep-ly in love, — But the

fu - le dray-fer - tl yor. —
sweet — thing got a - way. —

Shvartse karshelech raysn mir	Red cherries are not for picking,
Royte lozn mir shteyn.	Only the black ones are sweet.
Sheyne meydelech nemen mir,	We always choose the pretty girls -
Mi-se lozn mir geyn	They are nimble and fast on their feet -

Refrain:

Eyns tsvey, eyns tsvey dray -
Oy, vey iz tsu mir,
Vey iz tsu mayne yor -
A libe hob ich geshpilt
A fule dray-fertl yor.

Vos toygn mir di polke, mazurke,
Az tantsn, tants ich zey nit?
Vos toyg mir di sheyne figurke -
Az nemen, nemt zi mich nit - (Ref.)

Vos toygn mir di lipelech di sheyne
Az kushn, kushn zey mich nit?
Vos toygn mir di hentlech di kleyne
Az gletn, gletn zey mich nit - (Ref.)

Refrain:

One-two, one-two-three -
Oh, woe is to me,
Woe is to me, I say -
I fell so deeply in love -
But the sweet thing got away...

I cannot dance the Mazurka,
The Polka means nothing to me,
What's the use of my trying -
When the pretty girls won't have me!
(Ref.)

What good to me are her red lips?
I know they will never be kissing me -
What good to me are her little hands?
They'll not be caressing poor me. (Ref.)

Sheyn Bin Ich, Sheyn

I Am So Pretty

English text by Ruth Rubin,
© 1964 by Appleseed Music, Inc.

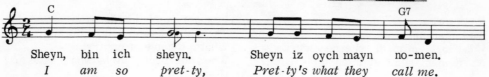

Sheyn, bin ich sheyn. Sheyn iz oych mayn no-men.
I am so pret-ty, Pret-ty's what they call me.

Redt men mir shi-du-chim mit groy-se ra-bo-nim. Ra-
Moth-er's look-ing for a rab-bi she wants me to mar-ry. The

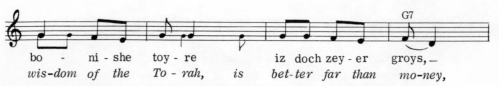

bo-ni-she toy-re iz doch zey-er groys, —
wis-dom of the To-rah, is bet-ter far than mo-ney,

Bin ich bay mayn ma-men a lich-ti-ge royz.
Moth-er's ve-ry proud of me, her sweet ros-y ho-ney.

Refrain

A sheyn may-de-le bin ich, Bloy-e ze-ke-lech trog ich,
Pret-ty pret-ty that am I, I wear socks blue like the sky,

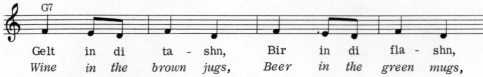

Gelt in di ta-shn, Bir in di fla-shn,
Wine in the brown jugs, Beer in the green mugs,

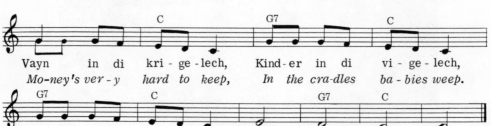

Vayn in di kri-ge-lech, Kind-er in di vi-ge-lech,
Mo-ney's ver-y hard to keep, In the cra-dles ba-bies weep.

Shray-en vi di tsi-ge-lech: Meh, Meh, Meh.
Like the lit-tle wool-ly sheep: Maa, Maa, Maa. _____

Shlof Mayn Kind, Shlof Keseyder

Sleep My Baby, I Will Croon to You

English text by Ruth Rubin,
©1964 by Appleseed Music, Inc.

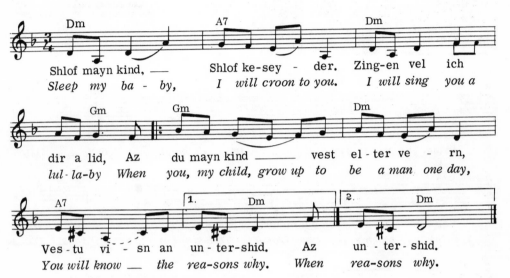

Shlof mayn kind, — Shlof ke-sey - der. Zing-en vel ich
Sleep my ba - by, *I will croon to you.* *I will sing you a*

dir a lid, Az du mayn kind —— vest el - ter ve - rn,
lul - la - by When you, my child, grow up to be a man one day,

Ves - tu vi - sn an un - ter-shid. Az un - ter - shid.
You will know — the rea-sons why. When rea-sons why.

Shlof mayn kind, shlof keseyder,
Zingen vel ich dir a lid,
Az du, mayn kind, vest elter vern,
Vestu visn an untershid.

Az du, mayn kind, vest elter vern,
Vestu vern mit laytn glaych,
Demlt vestu gevoyre vern,
Vos heyst orim un vos heyst raych.

Di shenste palatsn, di faynste hayzer,
Dos alts macht der oriman,
Nor veystu ver es tut in zey voynen?
Gor nit er, nor der raycher man.

Der oriman, er voynt in keler,
Der vilgotsh rint im fun di vent.
Derfun bakumt er rematiz feler,
In di fis un in di hent.

Sleep my baby, I will croon to you,
I will sing you a lullaby,
When you my child grow up to be a man
  one day,
You will know the reasons why -

The reasons why our world's divided,
Why the poor man lives in pain,
Why he toils upon the land from dawn
  to dusk,
And the rich man reaps the grain.

The fancy mansions, the finest houses,
Stand so proud upon the hill,
But the man who builds, does not inhabit
  them,
No, not he, but the rich man will.

Poor men are sick and pale with
  overwork.
Wondering why they were born,
To live in cellars that are cold and
  damp and drear,
To starve and tremble in clothing torn.

Trink Bruder, Trink Oys!

Drink Brother, Drink Up!

Mordche Gebirtig was the most popular tunesmith in Poland between World War I and II. He was put to death in 1942, during the German-Nazi occupation. Author of more than a hundred texts and tunes, many of Gebirtig's songs (written in folk style) achieved the widest currency among Yiddish-speaking communities. "Reyzele", "Yankele", "Motele", "Dos Shtetele Brent", "Hey Tsigelech", are but a few examples of his "folksongs".

Yiddish text and tune by Mordche Gebirtig. English text by Ruth Rubin, © 1964 by Appleseed Music, Inc.

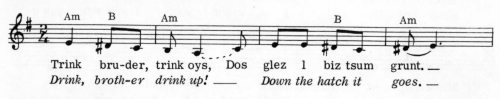

Trink bru-der, trink oys, Dos glez l biz tsum grunt. _
Drink, broth-er drink up! _ Down the hatch it goes. _

Ves tu ve-rn _ frish un mun-ter, Frey-lech un ge-zunt. Oy,
It helps us to for-get our trou-bles To bear our pain and _ woes. Oh

bru-der - l le - chay-im, Trink a bi-se-le vayn,
Pro-sit broth-ers le-chay-im, Lets drink a bit of _ wine,

Dos far-traybt di mo-re-sh'choy-re, ye - de zorg un payn. Oy,
That's what drives a - way the sor-row, Makes you feel so fine, Oh

Dos far-traybt di _ mo-re-sh'choy-re, ye - de zorg un _ payn.
That's what drives a - way the sor-row, Makes you feel so _ fine.

Trink bruder, trink oys,
Dos glezl biz tsum grunt.
Vestu vern frish un munter,
Freylech un gezunt.

Drink, brother, drink up!
Down the hatch it goes!
It helps us to forget our troubles,
To bear our pain and woes.

Refrain:

Oy, bruderl, lechayim,
Trink abisele vayn,
Dos fartraybt di more-sh'choyre,
Yede zorg un payn.

Itst bruder, trink ich,
Un vos felt mir atsind?
Ich fil zich gliklich vi a kenig,
Freylech vi a kind.

Itst bruder, trink ich,
Un ven es roysht in kop,
Fayf ich oyf der gantser velt
Un tants mir hop-hop-hop!

Refrain:

Oh Prosit, brothers, lechayim.*
Lets drink a bit of wine,
Thats what drives away the sorrow,
Makes you feel so fine!

When I drink up, boys,
I do not lack a thing,
I am happy as a youngster,
Mighty as a king.

When I keep drinking,
My head spins like a top,
I send my troubles to the devil,
And dance and skip and hop!

*Lechayim - the Jewish prosit. Literally it means
''To life''.

New-York, May 20, 1766.

Joy to AMERICA !

At 3 this Day arrived here an Expreſs from *Boſton*
with the following moſt glorious News, on which
H. Gaine congratulates the Friends of *America*.
Boſton, Friday 11 o'Clock, 16th May, 1766.
This Day arrived here the Brig *Harriſon*, belong-
ing to *John Hancock*, Eſq; Capt. *Shubael Coffin*,
in 6 Weeks and 2 Days from *London*, with the
following moſt agreeable Intelligence, *viz.*

Tsvey Taybelech

Two Little Doves

Love song. English text by Ruth Rubin, © 1964 by
Appleseed Music, Inc.

Tsvey tay-be-lech ze-nen i-ber-n vas-ser ge-floy-gn,
Two lit-tle doves___ were fly-ing a-cross___ the wa-ter,

Zey-e-re fli-ge-lech ho-bn zey tsu-shpreyt.
Their wings out-spread ___ high up a-bove.

ho-bn zey tsu-shpreyt. Far-shol-tn zol ve-rn ye-ner
high up a-bove. I curse that per-son, so ___

mentsh oyf der velt, ___ Vos er hot undz in undzer li-be, Oy ___
wick-ed, so cruel, ___ Who came be-tween you and me, my ___

vey, tsu-sheydt.
own true love.

Tsvey taybelech zenen ibern vasser
  gefloygn,
Zeyere fligelech hobn zey tsushpreyt.
Farsholtn zol vern yener mentsh oyf der
  velt,
Vos er hot undz in undzer libe, oy vey,
  tsusheydt.

Two little doves were flying across the
  wide water,
Their wings outspread high up
  above.
I curse that person, so wicked, so cruel
Who came between you and me, my own
  true love.

Un az du vest kumen in a vaytn land,
  lubelu,
In mayne verter zolstu zich badenken,
Un az du vest kumen iber a tifn vasser
  lubelu,
Far groys tsores zolstu zich nisht
  dertrenken.

Un az du vest kumen in a vaytn land,
  lubelu,
Mayne verter zolstu bakenen.
Un az du vest kumen iber a groysn
  fayer, lubelu,
Far groys tsores zolstu zich nisht
  farbrenen.

Tsvey taybelech zenen ibern vasser
  gefloygn,
In di piskelech hobn zey zich gekisht.
Farsholtn zol vern yener mentsh oyf der
velt,
Vos er hot zich in undzer libe, oy,
  arayngemisht.

And when you will come to that strange
  city so far away,
Remember the warnings of my heart -
And when you will come upon a deep,
  wide water,
Don't drown your sorrow there, now that
  we're apart.

And when you will come to that strange
  land so far away,
Remember the words that I said.
And if you should come upon a fire
  that's burning,
Don't wish then, my own true love,
  that you were dead.

Two little doves were flying across the
  wide water,
Cooing and kissing above.
I curse that person so wicked, so cruel
Who came between you and me, my own
  true love.

Yeder Ruft Mich Ziamele

People Call Me Ziamele

Collected by Ruth Rubin. English text by Ruth Rubin,
©1964 by Appleseed Music, Inc.

Ye-der ruft mich Zia-me-le, Ay, vi mir iz shver.
Peo-ple call me Zia-me-le, I live all a-lone.

Ch'ob ge-hat a ma-me-le, Ch'ob zi shoyn nit mer.
Once I had a moth-er dear, But she's dead and gone.

Ch'ob ge-hat a ta-te-le, Hot er mich ge-hit,
I am beat-en like a dog, Be-cause I am a Jew,

Itst bin ich a shma-te-le, Vayl ich bin a yid.
Yet once I had the best of care, A good kind fa-ther too.

Yeder ruft mich Ziamele,
Ay, vi mir iz shver.
Ch'ob gehat a mamele,
Ch'ob zi shoyn nit mer.
Ch'ob gehat a tatele,
Hot er mich gehit.
Itst bin ich a shmatele,
Vayl ich bin a yid.

People call me Ziamele,
I live all alone.
Once I had a mother dear,
But she's dead and gone.
I am beaten like a dog,
Because I am a Jew.
Yet once I had the best of care,
A good, kind father too.

Ch'ob gehat a shvesterl,
Iz zi mer nishto.
Oy, vu biztu Esterl?
In der shverer sho.
Ergets ba a beymele,
Ergets ba a ployt.
Ligt mayn bruder shloymele,
Fun a daytsh getoyt.

I had a little sister then,
I don't know where she's gone.
Oh, where are you Esterl?
I'm scared to be alone.
Somewhere near a wooden fence,
On the ground so bare,
Lies my brother Shloymele,
A German shot him there.

Ch'ob gehat a heymele,
Itster iz mir shlecht.
Ch'bin vi a beheymele,
Vos der talyen shecht.
Ach du got in himele,
Kuk af der erd arop,
Ze nor vi dayn blimele,
Shnaydt der talyen op.

Once I had a cozy home,
Now on the ground I lie.
We are slaughtered just like sheep,
No one hears our cry.
Oh, dear God, look down on us,
And see our people slain.
The Germans butcher little ones,
There's no end to our pain.

Yomi, Yomi

Dancing song. English text by Ruth Rubin, © 1964 by Appleseed Music, Inc.

Yo - mi, Yo - mi, zing mir a li - de - le Vos dos mey - de - le
Yo - mi, Yo - mi, why are you sigh - ing? Why are you sigh - ing my

vil? Dos mey - de - le vil a kley - de - le ho - bn,
dear? If a new dress is my Yo - mi's de - sire, — The

Darf men geyn der shnay - der - n zo - gn. Neyn, ma - me - shi,
fin - est seam - stress I will - hire. — No, moth - er dear,

neyn, Du veyst nit vos ich meyn, Du kenst mich nit far - shteyn.
no, My heart you do not know, A dress won't heal my woe.

Yomi, Yomi, zing mir a lidele
Vos dos meydele vil?
-Dos meydele vil a kleydele hobn,
Darf men geyn der shnaydern zogn -

Refrain:

Neyn, mameshi neyn,
Du veyst nit vos ich meyn,
Du kenst mich nit farshteyn.

Yomi, Yomi, zing mir a lidele
Vos dos meydele vil?
-Dos meydele vil a por shichelech hobn,
Darf men geyn dem shusterl zogn -
(Ref.)

Yomi Yomi...
Dos meydele vil a hitele hobn,
Darf men geyn der putserin zogn -
(Ref.)

Yomi, Yomi,...
-Dos meydele vil a por oyringlech
   hobn,
Darf men geyn dem goldshmid zogn -
(Ref.)

Yomi, Yomi,...
-Dos meydele vil a chosndl hobn,
Darf men geyn dem shadchendl zogn -

Final Refrain:

Yo, mameshi yo,
Du veyst shoyn vos ich meyn,
Du kenst mich shoyn farshteyn!

Yomi, Yomi, why are you crying,
Why are you sighing my dear?
-If a new dress is my Yomi's desire-
The finest seamstress I will hire-

Refrain:

No, mother dear, no,
My heart you do not know
A dress won't heal my woe.

Yomi, Yomi, why are you crying,
Why are you sighing my dear?
-If new shoes are my Yomi's desire,
The finest cobbler, I will hire -

Refrain:

(...Shoes won't heal my woe.)

Yomi, Yomi,...
-If a new hat is my Yomi's desire,
The finest milliner I will hire -

Refrain:

(...A hat won't heal my woe.)

Yomi, Yomi...
-If gold earrings are my Yomi's desire,
The finest goldsmith I will hire -

Refrain:

(...Earrings won't heal my woe.)

Yomi, Yomi,...
-If a bridegroom is my Yomi's desire-
The finest matchmaker I will hire -

Final Refrain:

Yes, mother dear, yes,
Now I must confess,
I want a husband, yes!

Yoshke Fort Avek

Yoshke's Going Off to War

This song originated in Vilna, Lithuania and is about an underworld character, "Yoshke", who preyed upon the small merchants in the Jewish quarter there. When the Russo-Japanese War broke out in 1904 and he was drafted, this satirical-humorous song describing an imaginary conversation between Yoshke and his lady-love, became popular. With the passage of time, however, folks began to interpret this song differently, with emphasis on the poignancy of separation in wartime. Both forms of interpretation are current.

Conversation song. English lyrics by Ruth Rubin,
© 1964 by Appleseed Music, Inc.

Bak mir nit kayn bul - ke-lech, Ich vel zay doch nit e - sn,
Bake no hon-ey buns for me, for - get you ev - er met me,

Ich for a-vek — fon-yen di - nen, Vest in mir far - ge - sn.
To the ar-my I must go, Oh, dar-ling don't for - get me!

Oy, — Oy, — Oy, — Oy,— Yosh - ke fort a - vek.
Oh, — Oh, — Oh, — Oh, — In an hour or so,

Noch a sho un noch a sho der poy-ezd geyt a - vek.
Yosh - ke's go - ing off to war, to the ar - my he must go.

Bak mir nit kayn bulkelech,
Ich vel zey doch nit esn.
Ich for avek fonyen dinen,
Vest in mir fargesn!

Refrain:

Oy, oy, oy, oy,
Yoshke fort avek.
Noch a sho un noch a sho,
Der poyezd geyt avek.

(He:)
Bake no honey buns for me,
Forget you ever met me -
To the army I must go,
Oh darling don't forget me!

Refrain:

Oh, oh, oh, oh,
In an hour or so,
Yoshke's going off to war,
To the army he must go.

Koyf mir nit kayn lokenes,
Un mach mich nit sheyn.
Koyf dir a por shtivelech,
Tsum priziv darfstu geyn.

Refrain:

Oy, oy, oy, oy,
Yoshke fort avek.
Lomir zich gezegenen,
Der poyezd geyt avek.

Klog-zhe nit un veyn-zhe nit,
S'iz altsding blote!
Ich vel zayn bay fonyen,
Der shenster in der rote!

Refrain:

Oy, oy, oy, oy,
Yoshke fort avek.
Noch a kush un noch a kush,
Der poyezd`geyt avek.

Di ban iz shoyn gekumen
Un es chapt mich on a shrek!
Oy, vey, mamenyu,
Yoshke fort avek.

Refrain:

Oy, oy, oy, oy,
Yoshke fort avek
Lomir zich gezegenen,
Der poyezd geyt avek....

(She:)
Buy no pretty things for me,
What do I need them for?
Get yourself some army boots,
You're marching off to war -

Refrain:

Oh, oh, oh, oh,
My tears are flowing free,
Come back safely, my true love,
Oh, darling think of me!

(He:)
Don't you weep and don't you cry
The army's just a ball -
In the regiment I'll be,
The handsomest of all....

Refrain:

Oh, oh, oh, oh,
In an hour or so,
Come my darling, kiss me now,
The train's about to go...

(She:)
The train is moving out at last,
Oh, darling, how I grieve!
I cannot bear to see you go,
How can I see you leave?

Refrain:

Oh, oh, oh, oh,
Help me mother dear,
My true love has gone to war
For many a weary year.....

Zhamele

The sardonic tone of this song is evident.

Lullaby, melody anonymous. Yiddish text by A. Litwin (1862-1943). English text by Ruth Rubin, ©1964 by Appleseed Music, Inc.

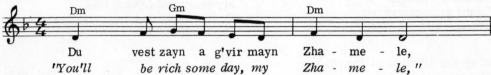

Du vest zayn a g'vir mayn Zha - me - le,
"You'll be rich some day, my Zha - me - le,"

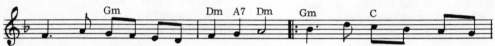

Fleg mir zing-en bay mayn vi - ge - le. A - le nacht a - mol mayn
At my cra-dle moth-er sang to me. Ev - ery night she'd croon the

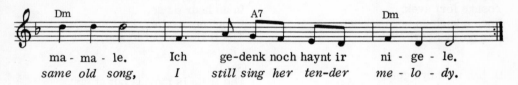

ma - ma - le. Ich ge-denk noch haynt ir ni - ge - le.
same old song, I still sing her ten-der me - lo - dy.

Du vest zayn a g'vir, mayn Zhamele,
Fleg mir zingen bay mayn vigele,
Ale nacht amol, mayn mamele,
Ich gedenk noch haynt ir nigele.

Un mekuyim iz gevorn mir,
Di havtoches fun mayn mamele,
Shver tsu gefinen aza groysn g'vir,
Aza'n oysher vi Zhamele.

shlofn, shloft er oyf a kerbele,
Macht hamoytse oyf a skorinke,
Un lechayim fun a sherbele
Trinkt er brunim-vasser klorinke.

Un di kinderlech, dos vaybele,
Geyen oysgeputst antikele!
Ful mit lates iz dos laybele,
Arumgegartlt mit a shtrikele...

"You'll be rich some day, my Zhamele",
At my cradle, mother sang to me.
Every night she'd croon the same old song,
I still sing her tender melody.

At last, my mother's dreams have all come true,
Her fond wishes and great hopes for me—
I'm the wealthiest in all the land,
My riches are so plain for all to see...

I sleep each night without a single care,
On a bed of straw I lay my head,
I drink spring water from a broken shard,
Make my blessing on a crust of bread.

And my loving wife and family,
In rags and patches, in the latest style,
They're still singing mother's melody:
"You'll be rich some day, my darling child..."

Zits Ich Mir Oyfn Benkele

On a Stool, One Summer's Day

Teasing song. English text by Ruth Rubin, © 1964
by Appleseed Music, Inc.

Zits ich mir oyf-n ben-ke-le, Un far-kem mir may-ne
On a stool ___ one sum-mer's day, Comb-ing my hair I heard a

he-re-lech. Geyt far-bay, oy, a shnay-der yung ___
tai-lor say: She's a hus-sy but she's caught my eye ___

Un zogt az ich bin nit er - lech!
So he teased me and made me sigh.

Zits ich mir oyfn benkele,
Un farkem mir mayne herelech,
Geyt farbay, oy, a shnayder-yung,
Un zogt az ich bin nit erlech.

Er zogt az s'iz tint,
Un ich zog az s'iz penes!
Er zogt az er hot mich lib –
Un ich zog az s'iz nit emes!

Zits ich mir oyfn fensterl,
Un farflecht mir mayne herelech,
Geyt farbay, oy, a shuster-yung,
Un zogt az ich bin nit erlech!

Er zogt az s'iz ash,
Un ich zog az s'iz koyln!
Er zogt az er vet mich nemen –
Un ich zog er vet nit poyln!

On a stool, one summer's day,
Combing my hair, I heard a tailor say:
She's a hussy but she's caught my eye -
So he teased me and made me sigh...

He said: ink is what you need my dear.
I said: no, its pens and that is clear!
He said: darling, I love but you -
I said: I don't believe you!

At my window, the other day,
Braiding my hair, I heard a cobbler say:
She's a hussy but she's caught my eye -
So he teased me and made me cry...

He said: ashes are very grey,
Burning coal is red-hot, I did say.
He said: darling will you marry me -
I said: Oho! we shall see!

Zhankoye

Dzhankoye was a depot in the Crimea, to which the Jewish collective farmers from the surrounding region would bring their produce. During the German occupation, the entire region was burnt to the ground.

Soviet-Yiddish folksong. English text by Ruth Rubin, © 1964 by Appleseed Music, Inc.

Az men fort kayn Se-vas-to-pl, Iz nit vayt fun Sim-fer-o-pl,
When you go to Se-vas-to-pol, Its not far from Sim-fer-o-pol,

Dor-tn iz a stan-tsi-ye far-an. Ver darf zuch-n
There's a de-pot in ___ the ___ sun. No need now to

nay-e glikn? S'iz a stan-tsi-ye an an-tik-l, In Zhan-koy-e,
be a rov-er All the fields here are in clo-ver, In Zhan-koy-e,

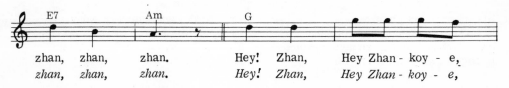

zhan, zhan, zhan. Hey! Zhan, Hey Zhan-koy-e,
zhan, zhan, zhan. Hey! Zhan, Hey Zhan-koy-e,

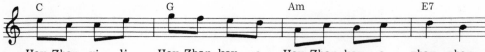

Hey Zhan-vi-li, Hey Zhan-koy-e, Hey Zhan-koy-e zhan, zhan,
Hey Zhan-vi-li, Hey Zhan-koy-e, Hey Zhan-koy-e zhan, zhan,

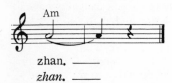

zhan. ———
zhan. ———

Az men fort kayn sevastopl,	When you go to Sevastopol,
Iz nit vayt fun simferopl,	Its not far from Simferopol,
Dortn iz a stantsiye faran.	There's a depot in the sun.
Ver darf zuchn naye glikn?	No need now to be a rover,
S'iz a stantsiye an antikl!	All the fields here are in clover,
In Zhankoye, zhan, zhan, zhan,	In Zhankoye, zhan, zhan, zhan.

Refrain:

Hey, zhan, hey, zhankoye,
Hey zhanvili, hey, zhankoye,
Hey, zhankoye, zhan, zhan, zhan.

Enfert yidn af mayn kashe,
Vu'z mayn bruder, vu'z abrashe,
S'geyt ba im der trakter vi a ban.
Di mume Leye ba der kosilke,
Beyle ba der molotilke,
In Zhankoye, zhan, zhan, zhan.

Ver zogt az yidn kenen nor handlen,
Esn fete yoych mit mandlen,
Nor nit zayn kayn arbetsman!
Dos konen zogn nor di sonim!
Yidn - shpayt zey on in ponim!
Tut a kuk oyf zhan, zhan, zhan.

Refrain:

Hey, zhan, hey, zhankoye,
Hey, zhanvili, hey, zhankoye,
Hey zhankoye, zhan, zhan, zhan.

Shout it brothers, you can bellow:
Abrasha is a handsome fellow!
He keeps that tractor on the run.
Bella's threshing, Leah's reaping,
There's no time for sighs and weeping,
In Zhankoye, zhan, zhan, zhan.

Some say Jews are only traders,
Can't work hard, are poor creators,
This slander's old beneath the sun.
For centuries for land we're thirsting,
Our silos now are full to bursting,
In Zhankoye, zhan, zhan, zhan.

Zog Nit Keynmol!

We Survive!

Hirsh Glik, poet of Vilna, was confined to the concentration camp Vayse Vake during the German occupation of World War II. In 1943, he joined the partisans and when the news of the Warsaw Ghetto uprising reached Vilna, he wrote this song. It immediately became the official hymn of the Jewish underground Partisan brigades. When the ghetto was liquidated, Glik was caught by the Gestapo and sent to a concentration camp in Esthonia. During the Red Army's offensive in the Baltic area, Glik escaped from the camp to the nearby woods, where he died fighting the Germans.

Text by Hirsh Glik (1920-1943). English text by Ruth Rubin, ©1964 by Appleseed Music, Inc.

Zog nit keyn-mol az du geyst dem lets-tn veg,
We must nev - er lose our cour-age in the fight,
Chotsh him-len
Though skies of

blay - e - ne far-shtel - n bloy - e teg.
lead turn days of sun-shine in - to night.
Ku - men
Be-cause the

vet noch un - dzer oys - ge-benk - te sho,
hour for which we've yearned will yet ar - rive,
S'vet a
And our

poyk ton un - dzer trot, mir ze - nen do!
march - ing steps will thun - der: We sur - vive!
Ku - men
Be-cause the

vet noch un - dzer oys - ge-benk - te sho,
hour for which we've yearned will yet ar - rive,
S'vet a
And our

poyk ton undz - er trot, mir ze - nen do!
march - ing steps will thun der: We sur - vive!

Zog nit keynmol az du geyst dem letstn
    veg,
Chotsh himlen blayene farshteln bloye
    teg,
Kumen vet noch undzer oysgebenkte
    sho,
S'vet a poyk ton undzer trot - mir zenen
    do!

Fun grinem palmen-land biz vaytn land
    fun shney,
Mir kumen on mit undzer payn, mit
    undzer vey,
Un vu gefaln s'iz a shprits fun undzer
    blut,
Shprotsn vet dort undzer gvure, undzer
    mut.

S'vet di morgn-zun bagildn undz dem
    haynt,
Un der nechtn vet farshvindn mitn faynt,
Nor oyb farzamen vet di zun un der
    kayor -
Vi a parol zol geyn dos lid fun dor tsu
    dor.

Dos lid geshribn iz mit blut un nit mit
    blay,
S'iz nit kayn lidl fun a foygl oyf der
    fray,
Dos hot a folk tsvishn falndike vent,
Dos lid gezungen mit naganes in di hent.

To zog nit keynmol az du geyst dem
    letstn veg,
Chotsh himlen blayene farshteln bloye
    teg,
Kumen vet noch undzer oysgebenkte
    sho,
S'vet a poyk ton undzer trot - mir
    zenen do!

We must never lose our courage in the
    fight,
Though skies of lead turn days of sun-
    shine into night.
Because the hour for which we've
    yearned will yet arrive,
And our marching steps will thunder:
    we survive!

From land of palm trees to the land of
    distant snow,
We have come with our deep sorrow
    and our woe,
And everywhere our blood was inno-
    cently shed,
Our fighting spirits will again avenge
    our dead.

The golden rays of morning sun will
    dry our tears,
Dispelling bitter agony of yesteryears,
But if the sun and dawn with us will be
    delayed-
Then let this song ring out the call to
    you, instead.

Not lead, but blood inscribed this song
    which now we sing,
Its not a caroling of birds upon the wing,
But a people midst the crashing fires of
    hell,
Sang this song and fought courageous
    till it fell!

So we must never lose our courage in the
    fight,
Though skies of lead turn days of
    sunshine into night.
Because the hour for which we've
    yearned will yet arrive,
And our marching steps will thunder:
    We survive!

Zolst Azoy Lebn Un Zayn Gezint

I'll Sing to the Baby and It Won't Cry

This baby-sitter is a little girl of no more than ten years old....

English text by Ruth Rubin, ©1964 by Appleseed Music, Inc. (Last stanza collected by Ruth Rubin.)

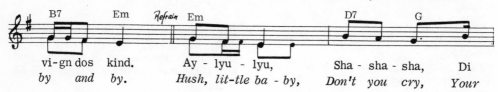

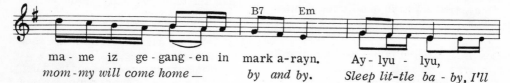

Zolst azoy lebn un zayn gezint,
Vi ich vel dir zitsn un vign dos kind.

Refrain:
Ay-lyu-lyu, sha-sha-sha
Di mame iz gegangen in mark arayn.
Ay-lyu-lyu, shlof mayn kind,
Di mameshi vet kumen gich un geshvind.

Andere meydelech tantsn un shpringen,
Un ich darf dem kind lidelech zingen.
(Ref.)

Andere meydelech tsukerkelech nashn,
Un ich darf dem kind's vindelech vashn.
(Ref.)

Dayn mame iz a tshatshke aza yor af ir,
Az du shlofst nit ayn, shrayt zi af mir.
(Ref.)

I'll sing to your baby, it won't cry,
I'll wait till you come home, by and by.

Refrain:
Hush little baby, don't you cry,
Your mommy will come home by and by.
Sleep little baby, I'll sing you a song,
Your mommy will return, she won't be long.

Other little girls can romp and play,
But I must sing to baby all the day.

While other little girls eat sugar candies,
Your mother makes me scrub your dirty panties...

Your mother's a mean one, this I know,
If you don't go to sleep, she'll scold me so!

Vacht Oyf!

Awake!

Prominent labor poet of the 80's and 90's in the U.S.A., fourteen of Edelshtat's poems are known to have been set to music by anonymous composers, and widely sung by Jewish workingmen on both sides of the Atlantic.

Yiddish text by David Edelshtat (1866-1892), tune anonymous. English text by Ruth Rubin, ©1964 by Appleseed Music, Inc.

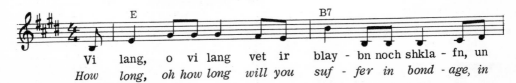

Vi lang, o vi lang vet ir blay - bn noch shkla - fn, un
How long, oh how long will you suf - fer in bond - age, in

tro - gn di shend - le - che keyt? Vi lang vet ir glents - n - de
sla - ver-y still to re-main? How long will you toil to cre-

raych - ti - mer sha - fn far dem vos ba - roybt - ay - er broyt? Vi broyt?
ate all the ri-ches for those who re-ward you with pain? How pain?

Vi lang, o vi lang vet ir blaybn noch shklafn
Un trogn di shendleche keyt?
Vi lang vet ir glentsende raychtimer shafn
For dem, vos baroybt ayer broyt?

Vi lang vet ir shteyn, ayer rukn geboygn,
Derniderikt, heymloz, farshmacht?
Es togt shoyn! vacht oyf un tsu-efnt di oygn!
Derfilt ayer ayzerne macht!

Klingt umetum in di frayhayts-glokn!
Farzamlt di laydende knecht!
Un kemft bagaystert, un kemft umder-shrokn,
Far ayere heylike recht!

Un ales vet lebn, un libn, un bli-en,
In frayen, in goldenem may!
Brider! genug far tiranen tsu kni-en,
Shvert, az ir muzt vern fray!

How long, oh how long will you suffer in bondage
In slavery still to remain?
How long will you toil to create all the riches
For those, who reward you with pain?

How long, oh how long will you carry the yoke
Of oppression and sorrow and fear?
Awaken! and see the new day that is dawning,
A free song is ringing mighty clear!

Ring out, bells of freedom, lets gather together
The suffering slaves in all lands,
Lets struggle for life and for love and for beauty,
Created by hardy toiling hands.

זשאנקריע (P. 80)

אז מען פארס קיין סעהאסטאפאל,
איז ניס ווים פון סימפעראפאל.
דארסן איז א סטאנציע פאראן.
ווער דארף זוכן נרע גליקן?
ס׳איז א סטאנציע, אן אנסיקל!
אין זשאנקריע, זשאן, זשאן, זשאן.

צוזינג:
היי זשאן, הי זשאנקריע,
הי זשאנווילי, הי זשאנקריע,
הי זשאנקריע, זשאן, זשאן, זשאן.

ענספערס אידן אויף מיך קשיא,
ואו׳ז מין ברודער, ואו׳ז אברא׳שע?
ס׳גיט בי אים דער סראקסאר ווי א
באן.
די סוסע לאה בי דער קאסילקע,
ביִלע בי דער מאלאסילקע,
אין זשאנקריע, זשאן, זשאן,
זשאן.

ווער זאגס אז אידן קענען נאר
האנדלען,
עס פעסע זיך מיס מאנדלען,
נאר ניס זין קין ארבעססמאן?
דאם קאנען זאגן נאר די שונאים,
אידן! שפרס זי אן אין פנים!
סוס א קוק אויף זשאן, זשאן,
זשאן!

זיץ איך מיר אויפן בענקעלע (P. 79)

זיץ איך מיר אויפן בענקעלע,
און פארקעם מיר מירנע הערעלעך,
גים פארבי, אוי, א שניידער-יונג,
און זאגס אז איך בין ניס ערליך.

ער זאגס אז ס׳איז סינס,
און איך זאג אז ס׳איז פענעס!
ער זאגס אז ער האס מיך ליב,
און איך זאג אז ס׳איז ניס אמת!

זיץ איך מיר אויפן פענסטערל,
און פארפלעכס מיר מינע הערעלעך,
גים פארבי, אוי, א חוססער-יונג,
און זאגס אז איך בין ניס ערליך!

ער זאגס אז ס׳איז אש,
און איך זאג אז ס׳איז קוילן!
ער זאגס אז ער וועס מיך נעמען,
און איך זאג ער וועס ניס פועלן!

זאג ניט קיינמאל (P. 82)

זאג ניס קיינמאל אז דו גיײַסס דעם לעצסן
וועג,
כאסס הימלען בליִענע פארסטעלן בלויע
סעג,
קומען וועס נאך אונדזער אויסגעבענקסע
שעה,
ס׳וועס א פויק סאן אונדזער סראס -
מיר זיינען דאן!

פון גרינעם פאלמען-לאנד ביז ווייסן
לאנד פון שני,
מיר קומען אן מיס מיס אונדזער פיין, מיס
אונדזער ווי,

און וואו געפאלן ס׳איז א שפראץ פון
אונדזער בלוס,
שפראצן וועס דארס אונדזער גבורה,
אונדזער מוס.

ס׳וועס די מארגן-זון באגילדן אונדז
דעם היינס,
און דער נעכסן וועס פארשווינדן מיס
פינס,
נאר אויב פארזאמען וועס די זון און
דער קאיאר,
ווי א פאראל זאל גין דאס ליד פון דור
צו דור.

דאס ליד געשריבן איז מיס בלוס און
ניס מיס בלי,
ס׳איז ניס קין לידל פון א פויגל
אויף דער פרי,
דאס האס א פאלק צווישן פאלנדיקע ווענס,
דאס ליד געזונגען מיס נאאגאנעס אין
די הענס.

סא, זאג ניס קינמאל אז דו גיסס דעם
לעצסן וועג,
כאסס הימלען בליִענע פארסטעלן בלויע
סעג,
קומען וועס נאך אונדזער אויסגעבענקסע
שעה,
ס׳וועס א פויק סאן אונדזער סראס -
מיר זיינען דאן!

זאלסט אזוי לעבן און זין געזונט (P. 84)

זאלסס אזוי לעבן און זין געזונס,
ווי איך וועל דיר זיצן און וויגן דאס
קינד.

צוזינג:
אי ליו ליו, שא-שא-שא,
די מאמע איז געגאנגען אין מארק
אריין.
אי ליו ליו, שלאף מין קינד,
די מאמעשי וועס קומען גיך און
געשווינד.

אנדערע מידעלעך סאנצן און שפרינגען,
און איך דארף דאס קינד לידעלעך
זינגען.

אנדערע מידעלעך צוקערקעלעך נאשן,
און איך דארף דעם קינד׳ס הינדעלעך
וואשן.

דין מאמע איז א טשאסטקע, אזא יאר
אף איר,
אז דו שלאפסס ניס אריין, שריס זי
אויף מיר.

86

(P. 72) יעדער רופֿט מיך זיאַמעלע

יעדער רופֿט מיך זיאַמעלע,
אַי, חי מיר איז שװער.
כ׳האָב געהאַט אַ מאַמעלע,
כ׳האָב זי שױן ניט מער.
כ׳האָב געהאַט אַ מאַמעלע,
האָט ער מיך געהיט.
איצט בין איך שמאַסעלע,
חײל איך בין אַ איד.

כ׳האָב געהאַט אַ שװעסטערל,
איז זי מער נישטאָ.
אױ, װאו בידזטו אסתרל,
אין דער שװערער שעה?
ערגעץ בײַ אַ בײמעלע,
ערגעץ בײַ אַ פֿליס,
ליגט מיַן ברודער שלמהלע,
פֿון אַ דײטש געטױטעט.

כ׳האָב געהאַט אַ הימעלע,
איצט איז מיר סלעכט.
כ׳בין װי אַ בהמהלע,
װאָס דער תליון שעכט.
אָך דו גאָט אין הימעלע,
קוק אױף דער ערד אַראָפ,
זע נאָר װי דיַן בלימעלע,
שניַדט דער תליון אָפ.

(P. 74) יאַמי, יאַמי, זינג מיר אַ לידעלע

יאַמי, יאַמי, זינג מיר אַ לידעלע,
װאָס דאָס מיידעלע חיל?
–דאָס מיידעלע װיל אַ קליידעלע האָבן,
דאַרף מען גײן דער שניַדערין זאָגן –

צוזינג:
נירן, מאַמעשי נירן,
דו חײסט ניט װאָס איך מײן,
דו קענסט מיך ניט פֿאַרשטײן.

יאַמי, יאַמי, זינג מיר אַ לידעלע,
װאָס דאָס מיידעלע חיל?
–דאָס מיידעלע װיל אַ פֿאַר שיכעלעך
האָבן,
דאַרף מען גײן דעם שוסטערל זאָגן –

צוזינג:
–דאָס מיידעלע װיל אַ היטעלע האָבן,
דאַרף מען גײן דער פוצערין זאָגן –

צוזינג:
דאָס מיידעלע חיל אַ פֿאַר אוירירינגלעך
האָבן,
דאַרף מען גײן דעם גאָלדשמיד זאָגן –

צוזינג:
דאָס מיידעלע חיל אַ חתנדל האָבן,
דאַרף מען גײן דעם שדכנדל זאָגן –

צוזינג:
יאַ, מאַמעשי יאַ,
דו חײסט שױן װאָס איך מײן,
דו קענסט מיך שױן פֿאַרשטײן!

(P. 76) יאַשקע פֿאָרט אַװעק

באַק מיר ניט קײן בולקעלעך,
איך װעל זי דאָך ניט עסן,
איך פֿאָר אַװעק פֿאַניעין דינען,
װעסט אין מיר פֿאַרגעסן.

אױ, אױ, אױ, אױ,
יאַשקע פֿאָרט אַװעק.
נאָך אַ שעה און נאָך אַ שעה,
דער פֿאַיעזד גײט אַװעק.

קױף מיר ניט קײן לאַקסענס,
און מאַך מיך ניט זאַרן.
קױף דיר אַ פֿאַר שטיװעלעך,
צום פֿריזיװ דאַרפסטו גײן.

אױ, אױ, אױ, אױ,
יאַשקע פֿאָרט אַװעק.
לאָמיר זיך געזעגענען,
דער פֿאַיעזד גײט אַװעק.

קלאָנג-זשע ניט און װײן-זשע ניט,
ס׳איז אלצדינג בלאָטע!
איך װעל זיַן בײַ פֿאַניע׳ן,
דער שענסטער אין דער ראָטע!

אױ, אױ, אױ, אױ,
יאַשקע פֿאָרט אַװעק.
נאָך אַ קוש און נאָך אַ קוש,
דער פֿאַיעזד גײט אַװעק.

די באַן איז שױן געקומען
און עס כאַפט מיך אָן אַ שרעק!
אױ, חי, מאַמעניו,
יאַשקע פֿאָרט אַװעק.

אױ, אױ, אױ, אױ,
יאַשקע פֿאָרט אַװעק.
לאָמיר זיך געזעגענען,
דער פֿאַיעזד גײט אַװעק...

(P. 78) ז שאַמעלע

דו װעסט זיַן אַ גביר, מיַן זשאַמעלע,
פֿלעג מיר זינגען בײַ מיַן חיגעלע,
אַלע נאַכט אַמאָל, מיַן מאַמעלע,
איך געדענק נאָך הײנט איר ניגעלע.

און מקױם איז געװאָרן מיר,
די הבטחות פֿון מיַן מאַמעלע,
שװער צו געפֿינען אַזאַ גרויסן גביר,
אַזאַ׳ן עושר װי זשאַמעלע.

סלאָפֿן, סלאָפֿט ער אױף אַ פֿערבעלע,
מאַכט המוצאי אױף אַ סקאָרינקע,
און לחיים פֿון אַ שערבעלע,
סרינגקט ער ברונים-װאַסער קלאָרינקע.

און די קינדערלעך, דאָס װירבעלע,
גיען אױסגעפוצט אַנטיקלעך!
פֿול מיט לאַטעס איז דאָס ליַבעלע,
אױמגענאַרטעלס מיט אַ סטריקעלע...

(P. 62) שפילט-זשע מיר דעם נײעם שער

צוזינג:
שפילט-זשע מיר דעם נײעם שער
װאָס איז אַרויסגעקומען,
איך האָב זיך פאַרליבט אין אַן אינגעלע
אַ שײנעם,
און קאָן צו אים ניט קומען.

כ'װאָלט צו אים געקומען,
װאוינט ער זייער װײַט,
כ'װאָלט דאָך אים אַ קוש געגעבן,
שעם איך זיך פאַר לײַט.
ניט אזוי פאַר לײַט,
װי פאַר גאָט אלײן,
כ'װאָלט מיט אים פאַרבראַכט די צײַט
אַז קײנער זאָל ניט זען.

קום-זשע צו מיר גיכער,
איך װאַרט אויף דיר שוין לאַנג.
קום-זשע גיך אַריבער,
מען זאָל ניט הערן דײַן גאַנג.
פיר איך דיך אין שטיבעלע
פון מײַן מאַמען אלײן,
חתן-כּלה װעלן מיר זײַן
און צו דער חופּה גײן.

(P. 64) שװאַרצע קאַרשעלעך רײַסן מיר

שװאַרצע קאַרשעלעך רײַסן מיר,
רויסע לאָזן מיר שטײן.
שײנע מײדעלעך נעמען מיר,
מיאוסע לאָזן מיר גײן.

צוזינג:
אײנס-צװײ, אײנס-צװײ-דרײ -
אוי, װי איז צו מיר,
װי איז צו מײַנע יאָר -
אַ ליבע האָב איך געשפילט
אַ פולע דרײַ-פערצל יאָר.

װאָס טויג מיר די פאַלקע, מאַזורקע,
אַז טאַנצן, טאַנצן איך זײ ניט?
װאָס טויג מיר די שײנע פיגורקע,
אַז נעמען, נעמען זי מיך ניט -

װאָס טויגן מיר די ליפּעלעך שײנע,
אַז קושן זײ מיך ניט?
װאָס טויגן מיר די הענדעלעך די שײנע,
אַז גלעטן, גלעטן זײ מיך ניט -

(P. 68) טרינק ברודער, טרינק אויס!

טרינק ברודער, טרינק אויס,
דאָס גלעזל ביז צום גרונט.
װעסטו װערן פריש און מונטער,
פרײלעך און געזונט.

צוזינג:
אוי, בדודערל, לחיים,
טרינק אַביסעלע װײַן,
דאָס פאַרטריבט די מרא שחורה,
יעדע זאָרג און פײַן.

איצט ברודער, טרינק איך,
און װאָס פעלט מיר אַצינד?
איך פיל זיך גליקלעך װי אַ קעניג,
פרײלעך װי אַ קינד.

איצט ברודער, טרינק איך,
און װען עס רוישט אין קאָפּ,
פײף איך אויף דער גאַנצער װעלט
און טאַנץ מיר דעם האָפּ-האָפּ-האָפּ!

(P. 70) צװײי טײבעלעך

צװי טײבעלעך זײַנען איבערן װאַסער
געפלויגן,
זײערע פליגעלעך האָבן זײ צושפּריט.
פאַרשאָלטן זאָל װערן יענער מענטש אויף
דער װעלט,
װאָס ער האָט אונדז אין אונדזער ליבע,
אוי װי, צושײדט.

און אַז דו װעסט קומען אין אַ װיסן
לאַנד, ליובעליו,
אין מײַנע װערסער זאָלסטו זיך באַדענקען.
און אַז דו װעסט קומען איבער אַ טיפן
װאַסער, ליובעליו,
פאַר גרויס צרות זאָלסטו זיך נישט
דערטרינקען.

און אַז דו װעסט קומען אין אַ װיסן
לאַנד, ליובעליו,
מײַנע װערטער זאָלסטו באַקענען.
און אַז דו װעסט קומען איבער אַ גרויסן
פײַער, ליובעליו,
פאַר גרויס צרות זאָלסטו זיך נישט
פאַרברענען.

צװי טײבעלעך זײַנען איבערן װאַסער
געפלויגן,
אין די פיסקעלעך האָבן זײ זיך געקושט.
פאַרשאָלטן זאָל װערן יענער מענטש אויף
דער װעלט,
װאָס ער האָט זיך אין אונדזער ליבע,
אוי, אַרינגעמישט.

(P. 85) װאַכט אויף!

װי לאַנג, אָ װי לאַנג װעט איר בלײַבן
נאָך שקלאַפן,
און טראָגן די שענדלעכע קײטס?
װי לאַנג װעט איר גלענצנדע רײַכטי-
מער שאַפן
פאַר דעם, װאָס באַרויבט אײַער ברויט?

װי לאַנג װעט איר שטײן, אײַער רוקן
געבויגן,
דערנידעריגט, הימלאַרץ, פאַרשמאַכט?
עס טאָגט שוין! װאַכט אויף און צו-
עפנט די אויגן!
דערפילט אײַער אײַזערנע מאַכט!

קלינגט אומעטום אין די פרײַהײַטס-
גלאָקן!
פאַרזאַמלט די לײַדענדע קנעכט!
און קעמפט באַגײַסטערט, און קעמפט
אומדערשראָקן,
פאַר אײַער הײליגע רעכט!

און אַלעס װאָס לעבן, און ליבן,
און בליהען,
אין פרײען, אין גאָלדענעם מאַי,
ברידער! גענוג פאַר טיראַנען צו
קניען,
שװערט, אַז איר מוזט װערן פרײַ!

לערנט קינדער, האָט ניט מורא,
יעדער אָנהויב איז שווער,
גליקלעך דער וואָס האָט געלערנט תורה,
צי דאַרף דער מענטש נאָך מער?

איר וועט קינדער, עלטער ווערן,
וועט איר אַלײן פֿאַרשטײן,
וויפֿיל אין די אותיות ליגן טרערן,
און וויפֿיל געוויין.

אַז איר וועט קינדער, דעם גלות שלעפּן,
אויסגעמוטשעט זײַן,
זאָלט איר פֿון די אותיות כח שעפּן,
קוקט אין זי אַרײַן!

פאפיר איז דאך ווײַס (P. 58)

פאפיר איז דאָך ווײַס און טינט איז דאָך שוואַרץ,
צו דיר מײַן זיס-לעבן, ציט דאָך מײַן האַרץ.
איך וואָלט שטענדיק געזעסן, דרײַ סעג נאָכאַנאַנד,
צו קושן דײַן שײן פנים און צו האַלטן דײַן האַנט.

נעכטן בין איך אויף אַ חתונה געווען,
פֿיל שײנע מײדעלעך האָב איך דאָרט געזען.
אײ, פֿיל שײנע מײדעלעך, צו דיר קומט ניט צו גאָר,
מיט דײַנע שוואַרצע אײגעלעך און מיט דײַנע שוואַרצע האָר.

אַך דו ליבער גאָט, הער אויס מײַן פֿאַרלאַנג,
דעם עושר גיסטו כבוד, מיס אַ שײנעם גאַנג,
אוי, מיר גיב אַ שטיבעלע אויף דעם גראַנד דעם גרינעם,
און איך מיט מײַן זיס-לעבן זאָל וואוינען דערינען.

שײן בין איך, שײן (P. 66)

שײן בין איך, שײן,
שײן איז אויך מײַן נאָמען,
רעדט מען מיר שידוכים
מיס גרויסע רבנים.

רבנישע תורה
איז דאָך זײער גרויס,
בין איך בײַ מײַן מאַמען
אַ לעקסיגע רויז.

אַ שײן מײדעלע בין איך,
בלויע זעקעלעך טראָג איך,
געלס אין די סאַשן,
בירן אין די פּלאַשן,

ווײַן אין די קריגעלעך,
קינדער אין די וויגעלעך,
שריען חי די ציגעלעך:
מע, מע, מעו.

שלאָף מײַן קינד, מײַן טרײַסט, מײַן שײנער (P. 60)

שלאָף מײַן קינד, מײַן טרײַסט, מײַן שײנער,
שלאָף-זשע זונעניו,
שלאָף מײַן קינד, מײַן קדיש אײנער,
שלאָף-זשע ליוליו.

בײַ דײַן וויגל, זיצט דײַן מאַמע,
זינגט אַ ליד און וויינט,
וועסט אַמאָל פֿאַרשטײן מסתמא,
וואָס זי האָט געמײנט.

אין אַמעריקע איז דער טאַטע,
דײַנער, זונעניו,
דו ביזט נאָך אַ קינד, לעת-עתה,
שלאָף-זשע, ליוליליו.

אין אַמעריקע איז פֿאַר יעדן,
זאָגט מען, גאָר אַ גליק,
און פֿאַר יעדן, אַ גן-עדן,
גאָר עפּעס אַן אנטיק.

דאָרטן עסט מען אין דער וואָכן,
חלה, זונעניו,
יאַיכעלעך וועל איך דיר קאָכן,
שלאָף-זשע, שלאָף, ליוליו.

ער וועט שיקן צוואַנציג דאָלאַר,
זײַן פּאָרטרעט דערצו,
און וועט נעמען, לעבן זאָל ער,
אונדז אַהינצוצו.

ער וועט קאָפֿן אונדז און קושן,
סאַנצן אַזש פֿאַר פֿרײד,
איך וועל קוואַלן טרערן גיסן,
ווײנען שטילערהײט.

ביז עס קומט דאָס גוטע קוויטל,
שלאָף-זשע זונעניו,
שלאָפן איז אַ טײער מיטל,
שלאָף-זשע, ליוליליו.

שלאָף מײַן קינד, שלאָף כסדר (P. 67)

שלאָף מײַן קינד, שלאָף כסדר,
זינגען וועל איך דיר אַ ליד,
אַז דו, מײַן קינד, וועסט עלטער ווערן,
וועסטו וויסן אַן אונטערשיד.

אַז דו, מײַן קינד, וועסט עלטער ווערן,
וועסטו מיס לײַטן גליך,
דעמאָלט וועסטו געוואויר ווערן,
וואָס הײסט אָרים און וואָס הײסט רײַך.

די שענסטע פּאַלאַצן, די פֿײַנסטע הײַזער,
דאָס אַלץ מאַכט דער אָרימאַן,
נאָר ווייסטו ווער עס טוט אין זי וואוינען?
גאָר ניט ער, נאָר דער רײַכער מאַן.

דער אָרימאַן, ער וואוינט אין קעלער,
דער ווילגאָטש רינט אים פֿון די ווענט,
דערפֿון באַקומט ער רעמאַטיז פֿעלער,
אין די פֿיס און אין די הענט.

מאכט ער מיר א סרובעצקע,
די סרובעצקע מאכט אזוי:
סרוטרוטרו, סרוטרוטרו,
אזוי מאכט די סרובעצקע!

מאכט ער מיר א צימבעלע,
דאָס צימבעלע מאכט אזוי:
צימצימצים, צימצימצים,
אזוי מאכט דאָס צימבעלע!

אַט אזוי נייט א שנידער (P. 50)

צוזינג:
אָט אזוי נייט א שנידער,
אָט אזוי נייט ער דאָך.

ער נייט און נייט א גאנצע וואָך,
פאָרדינט א גילדן מיט א לאָך.

א שנידער נייט און נייט און נייט,
פאָרדינט קדחות, ניט קיין ברויט.

פאראייאָרן, ניט הײַנט געדאַכט,
האָבן מיר געהאָרעוועס פון אכט ביז
אכט.

אָבער די סטרוקציע* האָט געמאַכט,
מיר האָרעווען שוין מער ניט פון
אכט ביז אכט.

* א פארקירצונג פון דעם וואָרט:
אבסטרוקציע.

אוי, א נאכט א שיינע (P. 52)

אוי, א נאכט א שיינע,
די נאכט איז געווען אזוי שיין,
אויף א בענקעלע זײַנען מיר געזעסן,
די לבנה האָט גענומען אחעקגיין.

אויף א בענקעלע זײַנען מיר געזעסן,
און האָבן צוזאמען פארבראכט.
וויפיל רייד מיר האָבן אינגע'סטענה'ס,
צו קיין סאלק האָבן מיר זיך ניט
דערטראכט.

וואָס-זשע פארא סאלק ליבע, ווילסטו?
אז איך מוז צו דעם פריזית שטײן.
קיין קנס-מאל קענען מיר ניט מאכן,
דאָס קענסטו דאָך אליין פארשטײן.

אויף באנגען וועל איך פאָרן,
און אויף וואסערן שווימען צו דיר.
כ'וועל פארלאָזן פאסער און מוטער,
און קומען, זיס-לעבן, צו דיר.

אויף קיין באנגען זאָלסטו ניט פאָרן,
און אויף וואסערן זאָלסטו ניט שווימען
צו מיר.
א חופה, אוי דושעניו, לאָמיר שטעלן,
און אין דרײַ יאָר וועל איך קומען צו
דירן.

אוי! דאָרטן, דאָרטן, איבערן וואסערל (P. 54)

אוי, דאָרטן, דאָרטן, איבערן וואסערל,
אוי, דאָרטן, דאָרטן, איבערן בריק.

פארטריבן האָסטו מיך אין די ווײַטענע
לענדער,
און בענקען, בענק איך נאָך דיר
צוריק.

אוי, וויפיל אָחנטסלעך, צוזאמען
געזעסן,
אוי, וויפיל אָחנטסלעך, שפעט אין דער
נאכט.
אוי, וויפיל סערעלעך, מיר האָבן
פאָרגאסן,
אוי, ביז מיר האָבן די ליבע צוזא-
מענגעבראכט.

אוי, דינע אויגעלעך, ווי די שוואַרצע
קאָרשעלעך,
דינע ליפעלעך, ווי די ראָזעווע
פאַפיר.
און דינע פינגערלעך, ווי סינט און
ווי פעדער,
אוי, שרײַבן זאָלסטו אָפטע בריוו צו
מיר.

אויפן באַרג און איבערן באַרג (P. 51)

אויפן באַרג און איבערן באַרג,
פליען טויבן פאָרן,
נאָך קיין נחת ניט דערלעבט,
שוין אחעק די יאָרן.

לאָמיר שפאנען פערד און וואָגן,
לאָמיר לויפן, פאָרן,
אפשר וועלן מיר דעריאָגן
אובדזערע יונגע יאָרן.

שוין דעריאָגט די יונגע יאָרן,
אויפן הויכן בריק.
-יאָרן, יאָרן, קערט זיך אום,
כאָטש אין געסט צוריק!

ניין, מיר וועלן זיך ניט אומקערן,
ס'איז ניטאָ צו וועמען
האָסט איר פריער ניט בעדאַרפס
אובדז אזוי פארשעמען!

אויפן פריפעטשאָק ברענט א פײַערל (P. 56)

אויפן פריפעטשאָק ברענט א פײַערל,
און אין שטוב איז הײַס,
און דער רבי לערנט קלײַנע קינדערלעך
דעם אלף-בית.

צוזינג:
זעט-זשע קינדערלעך, געדענקט-זשע
סירע,
וואָס איר לערנט דא.
זאָגט-זשע נאָך אמאָל און טאַקע נאָך
אמאָל:
קמץ-אלף: אָ!

לערנט קינדער, מיט גרויס חשק,
אזוי זאָג איך אײַך אָן.
ווער ס'וועט גיכער פון אײַך קענען
עברי,
דער באַקומט א פאָן.

צוזינג:
סאַנץ, סאַנץ, אַנטקעגן מיר,
און איך אַנטקעגן דיר –
דו חתסס נעסצן דעם איידים
און איך וועל נעמען די שניר!

צענבראַכן איז דער לאַקשנסטאָפ,
פאַרבראָכן דער נאָהיס –
סאַנצן די מחתנות'סעס,
די כלה אין דער מיט.

חתן'ס צד און כלה'ס צד –
די גאַנצע משפחה –
סאַנצן אויף דער חתונה
אין מזל און אין ברכה!

(P. 44) לאָמיר זיך איבערבעטן

לאָמיר זיך איבערבעטן, איבערבעטן,
וואָס שטיסטו בײַ דער סיר?
לאָמיר זיך איבערבעטן,
קום אַרײַן צו מיר.

לאָמיר זיך איבערבעטן, איבערבעטן,
וואָס שטיסטו בײַ מײַן פענסטער?
לאָמיר זיך איבערבעטן,
בײַזס בײַ מיר דער שענסטער.

לאָמיר זיך איבערבעטן, איבערבעטן,
קויף אַ פאָר מאראַנצן,
לאָמיר זיך איבערבעטן,
לאָמיר גיען סאַנצן.

לאָמיר זיך איבערבעטן, איבערבעטן,
סטעל דעם סאמאוואר,
לאָמיר זיך איבערבעטן,
זײַ-זשע נישט קיין נאַר.

לאָמיר זיך איבערבעטן, איבערבעטן,
לאָמיר נישט זײַן חי גרים.
לאָמיר זיך איבערבעטן,
לאמיר זײַן חברים.

(P. 45) גיי איך מיר שפּאַצירן

גיי איך מיר שפּאַצירן, טראַלאַלאַ, לאַלאַלאַ,
גיי איך מיר שפּאַצירן, טראַלאַלאַ,
לאַלאַלאַ, לאַ.
באַגעגנט זיך אַ בחור, אַהאַ, אַהאַ,
באַגעגנט זיך אַ בחור, אַהאַ!

ער זאָגט ער וועט מיך נעמען...
ער לייגט עס אָפ אויף ווינטער...

דער ווינטער איז געקומען...
ער האָט מיך נישט גענומען...

איצט וויל ער מיך שוין נעמען...
אַבער איך וויל אים נישט קענען!...

(P. 46) מײַן אינגעלע

איך האָב אַ קלײַנעם אינגעלע
אַ זונעלע גאָר פײַן.
ווען איך דערזע אים, דאַכט זיך מיר,
די גאַנצע וועלט איז מײַן.

נאָר זעלטן, זעלטן, זע איך אים,
מײַן שיינעם חען ער מאַכט.
איך טרעף אים אימער שלאָפענדיג,
איך זע אים נאָר בײַנאַכט.

די אַרבעט טרייבט מיך פרי אַרויס,
און לאָזט מיך שפּעט צוריק.
אַ פרעמד איז מיר מײַן אייגן לייב,
אַ פרעמד, מײַן קינד'ס אַ בליק.

איך קום צוקלעמטערהייט אהיים,
אין פינצטערניש געהילט,
מײַן בלייכע פרוי דערציילט מיר באַלד,
ווי פײַן דאָס קינד זיך שפּילט.

ווי זיס עס רעדט, ווי קלוג עס פרעגט:
אָ מאַמע, גוטע מאַ,
ווען קומט און ברענגט אַ פעני פּאַ,
מײַן גוטער, גוטער פּאַ?

איך הער עס צו, און יאָ, עס מוז,
יאָ, יאָ, עס מוז געשען!
די פאַטער-ליבע פלאַקערט אויף,
עס מוז מײַן קינד מיך זען!

איך שטיי בײַ זײַן געלעגערל,
און הער און זע און שאַ.
אַ טרוים באַוועגט די ליפּעלעך:
אָ וואו איז, וואו איז פּאַ?

איך קוש די בלויע אויגעלעך,
זיי עפֿענען זיך, אָ קינד!
זיי זעען מיך, זיי זעען מיך
און שליסן זיך געשווינד.

דאָ שטייט דײַן פּאַפּאַ, טײַערער,
אַ פּענעלע דיר, נאָ!
אַ טרוים באַוועגט די ליפּעלעך:
אָ וואו איז, וואו איז פּאַ?

איך בלייב צעחריסטאַגט און צוקלעמט,
פאַרביטערט, און איך קלער:
ווען דו ערוואַכסט אַמאָל, מײַן קינד,
געפֿינסטו מיך ניט מער...

(P. 48) סיכאַלקו

צוזינג:
האָב איך מיר אַ קלײַנעם סיכאַלקו,
סיכאַלקו,
וואוינט ער אויף דער לאַנגער גאַס.
מאַכט ער מיר וואָס ער וויל,
מאַכט ער מיר וואָס ער קען:

מאַכט ער מיר אַ פײַקעלע,
דאָס פײַקעלע מאַכט אַזוי:
סאַראַבאַבאַבאַבאַם, סאַראַבאַבאַבאַבאַם,
אַזוי מאַכט דאָס פײַקעלע!

מאַכט ער מיר אַ פּיפֿעלע,
דאָס פּיפֿעלע מאַכט אַזוי:
פֿלופֿלופֿלו, פֿלופֿלופֿלו,
אַזוי מאַכט דאָס פּיפֿעלע!

מאַכט ער מיר אַ פידעלע,
דאָס פידעלע מאַכט אַזוי:
פֿידל-דידל-דידל, לידל-דידל-דידל,
אַזוי מאַכט דאָס פידעלע!

איך לייד שטענדיג הונגער,
איך האָב ניט וואָס צו עסן,
וויל איך געלט בעסן,
הייסט מען מיר פֿאַרגעסן.

(P. 34) איין כלו אין כלו אין כל זיין

אין כל, אין כל, אין כל וויין...
כ׳קאָן אָן דיר ניט זיין.

אין כל, אין כל, אין כל ביר...
כ׳קאָן ניט זיין אָן דיר.

אין כל, אין כל, אין כל יש...
כ׳וויל אַ פֿולע פלאש.

אין כל, אין כל, אין כל קאָניאַק...
אַי, איז דאָס געשמאַק.

אין כל, אין כל, אין כל קוואַס...
כ׳וויל אַ פֿולע פאַס.

(P. 36) גיבן דיר מײן סאָכטער

גיבן דיר מײן סאָכטער, גיבן דיר מײן
סאָכטער.
אַ שוסטער פֿאַר אַ מאַן? אַ שוסטער פֿאַר
אַ מאַן?
-אַ שוסטער פֿאַר אַ מאַן, וויל איך ניט,
אַ שוסטער׳ס אַ סאָכטער בין איך ניט,
לאַטע שטיחל קאָן איך ניט.

ערשטער צוזינג:
זיך איך אויף אַ שטיין,
און קוק אַראָפ און חיין,
און זע חי אלע מיידעלעך האָבן חתונה,
און נאָר איך בלייב אַליין.

גיבן דיר מײן סאָכטער...
אַ שניידער פֿאַר אַ מאַן?...
-אַ שניידער פֿאַר אַ מאַן, וויל איך ניט,
אַ שניידער׳ס אַ סאָכטער בין איך ניט,
נייען קליידער קאָן איך ניט.

ערשטער צוזינג:
גיבן דיר מײן סאָכטער...
אַ למדן פֿאַר אַ מאַן?...
-אַ למדן פֿאַר אַ מאַן, וויל איך יאָ!
אַ למדן׳ס אַ סאָכטער, בין איך יאָ!
תורה לערנען קאָן איך יאָ!

צווייטער צוזינג:
זיך איך אויף דאַך,
און קוק אַראָפ און לאַך,
און זע חי אלע מיידעלעך האָבן חתונה,
און איך בין מיט זי גלייך!

(P. 38) האָב איך אַ פֿאַר אָקסן

האָב איך אַ פֿאַר אָקסן, אָקסן,
חאָס זי בראָקן לאַקשן, לאַקשן,
אי חאַונדער איבער חאַונדער,
חי די אָקסן בראָקן לאַקשן,
דאָס איז מיר אַ חאַונדער,
דאָס איז מיר אַ חאַונדער!

האָב איך אַ פֿאַר בערן, בערן,
חאָס זי סטיבער קערן, קערן,
אי חאַונדער איבער חאַונדער,
חי די בערן סטיבער קערן,
און די אָקסן בראָקן לאַקשן, א.א.וו.

האָב איך אַ פֿאַר ציגן, ציגן,
חאָס זי קינדער חיגן, חיגן,
אי חאַונדער איבער חאַונדער,
חי די ציגן קינדער חיגן,
און די בערן סטיבער קערן,
און די אָקסן בראָקן לאַקשן,א.א.וו.

האָב איך אַ פֿאַר הינס, הינס,
חאָס זי מאכן סינט, סינט.
אי חאַונדער איבער חאַונדער,
חי די הינס מאכן סינט,
און די ציגן קינדער חיגן,
און די בערן סטיבער קערן,
און די אָקסן בראָקן לאַקשן,א.א.וו.

האָב איך אַ פֿאַר הענער, הענער,
חאָס זי קלייבן שפפענער, שפפענער.
אי חאַונדער איבער חאַונדער,
חי די הענער קלייבן שפפענער,
און די הינס מאכן סינט,
און די ציגן קינדער חיגן,
און די בערן סטיבער קערן,
און די אָקסן בראָקן לאַקשן,
דאָס איז מיר אַ חאַונדער,
דאָס איז מיר אַ חאַונדער!

(P. 40) האָפ! מינע המנטאַשן

יאַקנע-דוואַשע פֿאָרט אין מאַרק,
זי האַלט זיך אין איין פאַקן,
פֿאָרט אויף פורים קויפן מעל,
המנטאַשן באַקן.

צוזינג:
האָפ, מינע המנטאַשן,
האָפ, מינע חייסע!
האָפ, מיט מינע המנטאַשן
האָט פֿאַסירט אַ מעשה!

ס׳גיט אַ רעגן, ס׳גיט אַ שניי,
ס׳קאַפפעט פֿון די דעכער,
יאַקנע פֿירט שוין קאַרנמעל,
אין אַ זאַק מיט לעכער.

ניט קיין האָניג, ניט קיין מעל,
און פֿאַרגעסן היוזן,
יאַקנע מאכט שוין המנטאַשן,
ס׳באַקט זיך שוין אין אויוון.

יאַקנע פֿירט שוין שלח-מנות,
צו דער באַבע יענטע,
צחיי-דרי המנטאַשן,
האַלב-רוי, האַלב-פֿאַרברענטע.

(P. 42) האָט זיך מיר די זיפ צעזיפט

האָט זיך מיר די זיפ צעזיפט
און האָט זיך מיר צעבראָכן.
האָט זיך מיר די שיך צעריסן,
סאָנץ איך אין די הוילע זאָקן!

די מיידעלע דו פיינס, דו מיידעלע דו
שיינס,
איך וועל דיר עפּעס פֿרעגן, א רעטעניש
א קלײנס:
וואָס פֿאַרא קײסער איז אָן א לאַנד?
און וואָס פֿאַרא וואַסער איז אָן אַ זאַמד?

דו נאַרישער בחור, דו נאַרישער כלאָפּ!
האָסט דאָך ניט קײן שכל אין דין קאָפּ!
-דער קײסער פֿון קאָרטן האָט ניט קײן לאַנד
טרערן פֿון די אױגן זײנען אָן אַ זאַמד.

עס איז געפֿלױגן די גילדערנע (P. 30)
פֿאָ חע

איז געפֿלױגן די גילדערנע פֿאָחע,
איבער אַלע ימען.
לאָז גריסן, דו גילדערנער פֿױגל,
מיין ליבער, האַרציגער מאַמען.

געפֿלױגן, געפֿלױגן די גילדערנע
פֿאָחע,
איבערן סיך, דעם גלאַטן.
לאָז גריסן, דו גילדערנער פֿױגל,
מיין ליבן, האַרציגן טאַטן.

געפֿלױגן, געפֿלױגן, די גילדערנע
פֿאָחע,
איבער אַלע פֿעלדער.
האָט זי פֿאַרלױרן דעם גילדערנעם
פֿעדער,
אין די פֿרעמדע לענדער.

ניט אַזױ די גילדערנע פֿעדער,
װי די פֿאָחע אַלײן.
ניט אַזױ דער פֿרעמדער זון,
װי די סאַכטער אַלײן.

װי עס איז ביטער, מיין ליבע מוטער,
א װאַסער אָן א פֿיש.
אַזױ איז ביטער, מיין ליבע מוטער,
בײ א פֿרעמדן טיש.

װי עס איז ביטער, מיין ליבע מוטער,
א פֿיגעלע אָן א נעסט.
אַזױ איז ביטער, מיין ליבע מוטער,
שװער און שוויגער'ס קעסט.

אײדער איך לײג מיך שלאָפֿן (P. 32)

אײדער איך לײג מיך שלאָפֿן,
דאַרף איך שױן אױפֿשטײן,
מיט מינע קראַנקע בינער,
צו דער אַרבעט גײן.

צוזינג:
צו גאָט וועל איך וויינען,
מיט גרױס געוויין;
וואָס בין איך געבױרן
א נישטאַרין צו זײן?

כ'קום שפּעט צו דער אַרבעט,
ס'איז דאַך חיץ דער וועג,
שלאָגנט מען מיר אָפּ
פֿאַר האַלבע טעג.

די נאָדלען ווערן צעבראָכן
פֿופֿצן א מינוט,
די פֿינגער ווערן צעשטאָכן,
עס רינט פֿון זי דאָס בלוט.

חאַצקעלע, חאַצקעלע (P. 25)

חאַצקעלע, חאַצקעלע,
שפּיל מיר א קאָזאַצקעלע,
כאַסט אָן אָרימע,
אבי א כװאָססקעץ.

צוזינג:
אָרים איז ניט גוט,
אָרים איז ניט גוט,
לאָמיר זיך ניט שעמען
מיט אײגענע בלוט.

ניט קײן געבעסטענע,
אַלײן געקױפֿען.
כאַסט אָן אָרימע,
פֿאָרט, א מומע!

חאַצקעלע, חאַצקעלע,
שפּיל מיר א דומע,
כאַסט אָן אָרימע,
אבי א פֿרומע!

דרעמלען פֿיגל אױף די צווייגן (P. 26)

דרעמלען פֿיגל אױף די צווייגן,
שלאָף מײן טײער קינד,
בײ דײן וויגל, אױף דײן נאַרע,
זיצט א פֿרעמדע און זינגט:
ליולינו, ליולינו, ליו.

ס'איז דײן וויגל חאו געשטאַנען,
אױסגעפֿלאָכטן פֿון גליק.
און דײן מאַמע, אױ דײן מאַמע,
קומט שױן קײנמאָל ניט צוריק.
ליולינו, ליולינו, ליו.

כ'האָב געזען דײן טאַטן לױפֿן
אונטער האַגל פֿון שטײן.
איבער פֿעלדער איז געפֿלױגן
זײן פֿאַר'יתומ'טער געוויין.
ליולינו, ליולינו, ליו.

דו מיידעלע דו פיינס, דו מיידעלע דו (P. 28)
שיינס

דו מיידעלע דו פיינס, דו מיידעלע דו
שיינס,
איך וועל דיר עפּעס פֿרעגן, א רעטעניש
א קלײנס,
וואָס איז העכער פֿון א הױז?
און וואָס איז פֿלינקער פֿון א מױז?

דו נאַרישער בחור, דו נאַרישער כלאָפּ!
האָסט דאָך ניט קײן שכל אין דין קאָפּ!
-דער רױך איז העכער פֿון א הױז,
א קאַץ איז פֿלינקער פֿון א מױז.

דו מיידעלע דו פיינס, דו מיידעלע דו
שיינס,
איך וועל דיר עפּעס פֿרעגן, א רעטעניש
א קלײנס:
וואָס פֿליט אָן פֿליגל?
און וואָס מויערט אָן ציגל?

דו נאַרישער בחור, דו נאַרישער כלאָפּ!
האָסט דאָך ניט קײן שכל אין דין קאָפּ!
-דער שני פֿליס אָן פֿליגל,
דער פֿראָסט מויערט אָן ציגל.

93

בייט-זשע מיר אויס א פינף-און-
צוואַנציקער,
אויף סאָמע אימפעריאַלן,
איך וועל בעטן די כלי-זמרים׳לעך,
זיי זאָלן זיך ניט אײַלן.

(P. 13) בין איך מיר א שנײַדערל

בין איך מיר א שנײַדערל,
לעב איך מיר טאָג אויס, טאָג אײַן,
לוסטיק און פרײלעך און פײַן.
-זאָג מיר שנײַדער, ליבינקער און גוטער,
גיט דיר די נאָדל, געגוג אויף ברויט
מיט פּוטער?
-איך מאַך א האָן, צוויי גילדן מיס א
דרײַער,
איך עס נאָר ברויט, חיל פּוטער איז
צו טײַער.

בין איך מיר א שוסטערל,
לעב איך מיר טאָג אויס, טאָג אײַן,
לוסטיק און פרײלעך און פײַן.
-זאָג מיר שוסטער, האָסטו וואָס צו
קײַען?
פעלט דיר אויסעס, האָסטו וואָו צו
לײַען?
-קינדער לייט ניטאָ, קינדער גיט קײן
אַרבות,
איך בין א שוסטער, גי איך סאַק׳ע
באַרוועס.

בין איך מיר א בלעכערל,
לעב איך מיר טאָג אויס, טאָג אײַן,
לוסטיק און פרײלעך און פײַן.
-זאָג מיר בלעכער, חי גרויס איז בי
דיר די נויט?
האָסטו בולקעס, האָסטו ניט קיין
ברויט?
-איך זיץ און קלאַפ בי יענעם פרעמדע
דעכער,
בי מיר אין שטוב רינט פון אַלע לעכער.

בין איך מיר א קרעמערל,
לעב איך מיר טאָג אויס, טאָג אײַן,
לוסטיק און פרײלעך און פײַן.
-זאָג מיר קרעמער, האָסטו מיט וואָס צו
האַנדלען?
האָסטו אין קרעמל ראָזשינקעס מיט
מאַנדלען?
-איך האָב אין קרעמל פאַר צוויי גראָשן
סחורה,
איך שלעפ דעם דלות און איך בענטש
דעם בורא.

(P. 20) בין איך מיר געגאַנגען פישעלעך קויפן

בין איך מיר געגאַנגען פישעלעך
קויפן,
האָב איך מיר געקויפט א העכט.
און וואָר עס איז שולדיג אין אונדזער
ליבע,
דער זאָל אויסגריען חי א ליכס!

צוזינג: די די די...
אַז א קאָרטיאאָזשיק שפּילט אין קאָרטן,
פאַרשפּילט ער דאַן נאָר זײַן געלט.
איך האָב פאַרשפּילט מײַנע יונגע יאָרן,
ינסטער איז דאָך מײַן וועלט.

אָן קײן ציגל און אָן קײן שטײַנער,
קאָן מען קײן הויז נישט מויערן.
אײַ, ס׳איז נישטאָ אזא מענטש אויף
דער וועלט,
וואָס ער זאָל מיך נישט באַדויערן!

(P. 22) בייזסטו מיט מיר ברוגז

בייזסטו מיט מיר ברוגז
חיס איך נישט פאַרוואָס?
גייס אַרום א גאַנצן טאָג
אַראָפּגעלאָזט די נאָז.

צוזינג: די די די...
און אפשר חילסטו חיסן
אַז איך האָב דיך ליב?
לאָמיר ביידע אריבערפאָרן
צו דעם גוטן יד.

צו דעם גוטן ידן
א פדיון אים אָפּגעבן,
וועס ער פאַר אונדז גאָס בעטן
פאַר א גוט לעבן.

און אַז מיר וועלן קומען
צוריק פון גוטן ידן,
וועלן מיר ביידע אריבערפאָרן
אין זעלוע אויף דעם יריד.

דאָרם וועל איך דיר קויפן
א זיידיגער מיט א קריט,
און א שיינע גרויס שטיק
זיידענס אויף א קלייד.

טאָ, זיי-זשע מער נישט ברוגז
און גריס אויף גיך צום טיש -
און זעץ זיך מיט מיר עסן,
באַקומסטו פון מיר א קוש!

(P. 24) בולבעס

זונטיק - בולבעס,
מאָנטיק - בולבעס,
דינסטיק און מיטוואָך - בולבעס
דאָנערשטיק און פרייטיק - בולבעס.
אָבער שבת אין א נאָוחינע, א בולבע
קוגעלעו!
און זונטיק ווײַטער, בולבעס.

ברויט מיס בולבעס,
פליש מיס בולבעס,
וואַרימעס און וועטשערע - בולבעס,
אָבער און חידער - בולבעס.
אָבער אײַנמאָל אין א נאָוחינע, א בולבע
קוגעלעו!
און זונטיק ווײַטער, בולבעס.

אָבער - בולבעס,
חידער - בולבעס,
אָבער און חידער - בולבעס,
חידער און אָבער - בולבעס.
אָבער שבת נאָכן טשאָלנט, א בולבע
קוגעלעו!
און זונטיק ווײַטער, בולבעס.

(P. 10) אמאל איז געווען א מעשה

אמאל איז געווען א מעשה,
די מעשה איז גאָרניט פריילעך
די מעשה הויבט זיך אָנעט
מיט א ייִדישן מלך.

צוזינג:
ליולינקע מײן פֿייגעלע,
ליולינקע מײן קינד.
כ'האָב אנגעוואוירן אזא ליבע,
ווי איז מיר און װינד.

דער מלך האָט געהאַט א מלכה,
די מלכה האָט געהאַט א װײנגאָרטן,
דער װײנגאָרטן האָט געהאַט א בוים,
ליולינקע מײן קינד.

דער בוים האָט געהאַט א צװײַג,
דער צװײַג האָט געהאַט א נעסטעלע,
אין נעסטעלע איז געהאַן א פֿייגעלע,
ליולינקע מײן קינד.

דער מלך איז אָפּגעשטאָרבן,
די מלכה איז געװאָרן פֿאַרדאָרבן,
דער צװײַג איז אָפּגעבראָכן,
דאָס פֿייגעלע פֿון נעסט אנטלאָפֿן.

װאו נעמט מען אזא חכם,
ער זאָל קענען די שטערן צײלן?
װאו נעמט מען אזא דאָקטער,
ער זאָל קענען מײן האַרץ הײלן?

(P. 12) אײלע ליולע ליולע ליולע

אײלע ליולע ליולע ליולע,
שלאָף-זשע, שלאָף מײן גדולה,
מאַך-זשע צו דײנע
אײגעלעך, די פֿינע.

און שטײ אויף װידער,
מיט געזונטע גלידער,
מײן ליב-זיס קינד,
גיך און געשװינד.

אין מאַרק װעל איך לויפן,
בײגעלעך װעל איך קויפן,
מיט פּוטער װעל איך שמירן,
צו דער חופה זאָל איך דיך פירן...

װעסט אויסװאַקסן א גרויסינקער,
װעסטו זײן א תנא!
װעלן דאַך אלע
זײן מיך מקנא!

(P. 16) בײ דעם שטעטל שטײט א שטיבל

בײ דעם שטעטל שטײט א שטיבל,
מיט א גרינעם דאַך.
און ארום דעם שטיבל װאַקסן
ביימעלעך א סך.

און דער סאטע מיט דער מאמע,
חנהלע מיט מיר,
שוין א לאַנגע צײט אינאײנעם
װאוינען אלע פֿיר.

און דער סאטע האָרעװעט, האָרעװעט,
אלע יאָרן זײנע,
און ער קויפט אונדז, און ער ברענגט
אונדז
זאכן שײנע, פֿײנע.

ברענגט א הינטעלע, װאָס סע האָװקעט,
מיסטן נאָמען צוציק,
ברענגט א פֿערדל װאָס סע הירזשעט,
מיסטן נאָמען מוציק.

ברענגט א גענדזעלע מיט א לאַנגן האַלדז
פֿעדערלעך װײס װי שנײ,
ברענגט א הון װאָס קװאָקעט, קװאָקעט,
ביז זי ליגט אן אײ.

נעמט די מאמע, אַס די אײער,
אָי, איז דאָס א מופת!
זעצט זי אויף **אויף** זי א קװאָקע,
האָבן מיר נײע **אויפֿות**

(P. 17) אויפֿן ים װײעט א װינטעלע

אויפֿן ים װײעט א װינטעלע,
און די כװאַליעס שלאָגן;
איך האָב זיך פֿאַרליבט אין א שײן
אינגעלע,
כ'האָב ניס פֿאַר װעמען צו זאָגן.

איך האב זיך געבאַװעט א שטיבעלע
אין װאַלד,
ארום און ארום מיט פֿענסטער,
פֿון אלע קאָרטי̈נקעס װאָס איך האָב
געזען,
ביזטו בײ מיר דער שענסטער!

צו ליבסטו מיך פֿון סיפֿן האַרצן,
צו ליבסטו נאָר מײן שײן פנים?
דו האַסט מיך נאָר גאַר אויועגעקוילעס,
אזוי װי די רעכסע גזלנים!

אז א גזלן קוילעט א מענטשן,
קוילעט ער אים מיט א מעסער.
האָסט מיך געקוילעט, און נישט
דערקוילעט,
ביזט פֿון א גזלן נאָך גרעסער!

(P. 18) בײט-זשע מיר אויס א פינף-און-צװאַנצי קער

בײט-זשע מיר אויס א פינף-און-
צװאַנציקער,
אויף סאמאראָדנע פֿירער,
און שפּילט-זשע מיר כליזמרים'לעך,
דאָס זעלביקע װי פֿריער.

צוזינג:
רימטשי... ראָם.

בײט-זשע מיר אויס א פינף-און-
צװאַנציקער,
אויף סאמאראָדנע דרײער,
און שפּילט-זשע מיר כליזמרים'לעך,
א לידעלע א טײער.

בײט-זשע מיר אויס א פינף-און-
צװאַנציקער,
אויף סאמאראָדנע צענער,
און שפּילט-זשע מיר כליזמרים'לעך,
דאָס זעלביקע נאָך שענער.

YIDDISH TEXTS

(P. 6) **א גנבה**

צוזינג:

ביי מײן רבין איז געוועזן,
איז געוועזן, ביי מײן רבין.
ביי מײן רבין איז געוועזן – א גנבה!

זיבן העמדער וי די בעכער
דרײ מיט לאטעס, פיר מיט לעכער.
ביי מײן רבין איז געוועזן
א גנבה!

צוזינג:

זיבן לײכטער וי די בערן,
דרײ אָן פיס און פיר אָן רערן.
ביי מײן רבין איז געוועזן
א גנבה!

צוזינג:

זיבן הענער וי די צינג,
דרײ אָן קעפ און פיר אָן פליגל.
ביי מײן רבין איז געוועזן
א גנבה!

צוזינג:

זיבן סעקטער וי די סאָסנעס,
דרײ אָן צײן און פיר אָן יאסלעס.
ביי מײן רבין איז געוועזן
א גנבה!

(P. 8) **אַף די פעלדער, גרינע פעלדער**

אַף די פעלדער, גרינע פעלדער, אױ-װײ,
אַף די פעלדער, גרינע פעלדער,
דאָרט ליגט פאַרהאָרפן א יונגער זעלנער,
אױ-װײ.
דאָרט ליגט פאַרהאָרפן א יונגער זעלנער,
אױ-װײ.

קומט א פױגל אָן צופליען, אױ-װײ,
אַף זײן קבר אָפצורוען, אױ-װײ.

אױ דו פױגל, פלי געשװינד,
און זאָג דער מאמען איך בין געזונט.

פון דעם סרים זאָלסטו איר ניט זאָגן,
װײל די װעט נעבעך חרגן און קלאָגן.

קומט דער פױגל צופליען אהײם,
און טרעפט זײן מאמען טרױעריק שטײן.

װי איז מיר, אױ װי און װינד!
ס'האָט פארטריבן מײן אײנציק קינד!

װען די זאָמד װעט צערונען װערן,
װעט זיך צו מיר מײן קינד אומקערן.

װען די זאָמד װעט אמאל אנטרינען,
איר קינד װעט שױן אהײם ניט קומען.

(P. 9) **אלע** װאסערלעך פליסן אװעק.

אלע װאסערלעך פליסן אװעק,
די גריבעלעך בלײבן לידיק.
ניסטא אזא מענטש אױף גאָר דער װעלט,
װאָס' זאָל פארשטײן מײן װײסיג.

די יאָרעלעך ציען, די יאָרעלעך פליען,
די צײט גײט אװעק װי רױך,
און אז איך דערמאָן זיך אָן דיר, מײן
זיס-לעבן,
גײט מיר אױס דער כח.

און אז א מײדעלע שפילט א ליבע,
שפילן אין איר אלע פאַרבן.
און אז זי שפילט איר ליבע ניט אױס,
קאָן זי חלילה נאָך שטארבן.

און אז די טעפעלעך טריקענען אױס,
בלײבן זײ אלע לידיג.
און אז א מײדעלע פירט איר ליבע ניט
אױס,
װערט זי פארפאלן אױף אײביג.